COMMUNITY
PSYCHIATRY

Proceedings of a Symposium on Community Psychiatry,

1964, sponsored by the University of Wisconsin

Department of Psychiatry, the Wisconsin Psychiatric

Institute, and the Wisconsin State Department of Public

Welfare, Division of Mental Hygiene.

COMMUNITY PSYCHIATRY

EDITED BY
LEIGH M. ROBERTS, SEYMOUR L. HALLECK,
AND MARTIN B. LOEB

THE UNIVERSITY OF WISCONSIN PRESS

MADISON, MILWAUKEE, AND LONDON, 1966

Published by
The University of Wisconsin Press
Madison, Milwaukee, and London
U.S.A.: Box 1379, Madison, Wisconsin 53701
U.K.: 26–28 Hallam Street, London, W.1

Printed in the United States of America
by Kingsport Press, Inc., Kingsport, Tennessee

Library of Congress Catalog Card Number 66–13806

Contributors

FRANCIS A. ALLEN, LL.B.
Dean of the Law School
University of Michigan, Ann Arbor, Michigan

ROBERT H. BARNES, M.D.
Executive Director, Greater Kansas City Mental Health Foundation
Kansas City, Missouri

F. E. COBURN, M.D.
Professor, Department of Psychiatry, University of Saskatchewan
Saskatoon, Saskatchewan, Canada

SEYMOUR L. HALLECK, M.D.
Professor, Department of Psychiatry
University of Wisconsin, Madison, Wisconsin

ALFRED J. KAHN, D.S.W.
Professor, School of Social Work
Columbia University, New York, New York

MARTIN B. LOEB, PH.D.
Professor and Director, School of Social Work
University of Wisconsin, Madison, Wisconsin

DAVID MECHANIC, PH.D.
Professor, Department of Sociology
University of Wisconsin, Madison, Wisconsin

MILTON H. MILLER, M.D.
Professor and Chairman, Department of Psychiatry
Director, Wisconsin Psychiatric Institute
University of Wisconsin Medical Center, Madison, Wisconsin

LEIGH M. ROBERTS, M.D.
Associate Professor, Department of Psychiatry
University of Wisconsin, Madison, Wisconsin

HOWARD P. ROME, M.D.
Senior Consultant, Section of Psychiatry, Mayo Clinic
Professor of Psychiatry, Mayo Foundation
University of Minnesota, Rochester, Minnesota

MILTON ROSENBAUM, M.D.
Professor and Chairman, Department of Psychiatry
Albert Einstein College of Medicine
Yeshiva University, New York, New York

MELVIN SABSHIN, M.D.
Professor and Head, Department of Psychiatry
University of Illinois, College of Medicine
Chicago, Illinois

H. G. WHITTINGTON, M.D.
Director of Psychiatry
Denver Department of Health and Hospitals
Denver, Colorado

J. K. WING, M.D., PH.D., D.P.M.
Director, Medical Research Council
Social Psychiatry Research Unit
Institute of Psychiatry, Maudsley Hospital
Denmark Hill, London, England

ISRAEL ZWERLING, M.D., PH.D.
Associate Professor, Department of Psychiatry
Albert Einstein College of Medicine
Yeshiva University, New York, New York

Foreword

THE term "community phychiatry" is a commonly used but often poorly defined expression in the field of psychiatry. Numerous definitions have been given, but without precise clarification its meaning is never certain. In the light of this ambiguity, a conference was held at the University of Wisconsin in Madison on June 24–26, 1964, on the theme "Community Psychiatry: What It Is and What It Is Not." The cosponsors were the University of Wisconsin Department of Psychiatry, the Wisconsin Psychiatric Institute, and the Division of Mental Hygiene, Wisconsin State Department of Public Welfare.

This conference brought together professional representatives of psychiatry, psychology, social work, sociology, education, and law to explore the general theme of community psychiatry. It is still too early to reach a consensus on a definition, and it is not clear whether this aspect of psychiatry, like child psychiatry, will perhaps ultimately form a subspecialty of the field. The proceedings of the conference are presented in this volume in the hope of shedding further light on these issues.

We wish to thank the editors of the *British Journal of Psychiatry* for permission to publish a figure from Dr. Wing's article, "Social

Treatment of Chronic Schizophrenia: A Comparative Survey of Three Mental Hospitals," co-authored with G. W. Brown, which appeared in the *Journal of Mental Science* (the former name of the *British Journal of Psychiatry*), 107 (1961), 856. Another figure in Dr. Wing's article was taken from "The Response of Severely Ill Chronic Schizophrenic Patients to Social Stimulation," co-authored with R. K. Freudenberg, which appeared in *The American Journal of Psychiatry*, 118 (1961), 316. Without exception, the papers in this volume are published here for the first time.

Mrs. Carol Clothier and Mrs. Nikki Swingle of the staff of the Wisconsin Psychiatric Institute have been invaluable in preparing the manuscripts for publication; to them we extend our deepest appreciation.

Madison, Wisconsin   L.M.R., S.L.H., M.B.L.
October, 1965

Contents

III   Community Psychiatry in Perspective

COMMUNITY

PSYCHIATRY

Introduction

LEIGH M. ROBERTS, M.D.

IT IS well known that advances in civilization occur as a product of evolving cultural patterns. This is equally true of scientific discovery, furtherance of man's freedom, and the emergence of new ideas in many fields of human endeavor. It is no coincidence that such events occur simultaneously with cultural shifts. The past two decades have seen an explosion of scientific knowledge unparalleled in history, and during this period comparably exciting events have occurred in other areas. A profound rise of nationalism has shaken off most of the shackles of Western colonialism that persisted from earlier centuries, and new nations have emerged, struggling to secure for themselves the right of self-determination. Human dignity has assumed a higher place as a right of man. The assertion of the Negro in this nation that he is deserving of first class citizenship and equal opportunity has come to the foreground in civil rights struggles. Following World War II, the philosophical premises of existentialism became increasingly prominent in Western Europe and spread to the United States. Simultaneously, new trends arose in the care of the mentally ill. The acceptance of the mentally ill as persons who retained humanity, and who therefore should be dealt with as

3

continuing members of the society from which they came, emerged as a premise of their treatment. This placed a premium on community care and treatment in the patient's home locale rather than in a distant and isolated institutional setting. There was greater concern that intensive treatment efforts be sustained until those previously regarded as hopelessly ill and in need of prolonged or indefinite confinement could be discharged back into their communities. Increased institutional staffs, enthusiasm for remotivating techniques to rekindle the spark of human warmth in chronic patients, and later the development of psychotropic drugs succeeded in altering patterns of institutional care in Western Europe and in the United States. Programs of day care and night care, halfway houses, vocational rehabilitation, and continuity and co-ordination of aftercare resources emerged, resulting in a progressive decrease in the numbers of persons confined in public mental hospitals. In the midst of this, attention has shifted from institutional psychiatry to psychiatric practice within the community; the community has become a focal point of prevention, therapy, and rehabilitation. A striking aspect of this shift has been a simultaneous interest in the community not only on the part of psychiatrists and other mental health professionals, but by attorneys, physicians, clergymen, politicians, industrialists, and social scientists, among others.

This societal concern for the community and the health of its constituents is the background against which community psychiatry has emerged. One of the manifestations of this pattern was the appointment by Congress in 1955 of the Joint Commission on Mental Illness and Health. Their report, *Action for Mental Health* (6), published in 1961, further set the stage for federal and state legislative action to provide increased local care of the mentally ill in the community. Recent state mental health planning has carried this trend still farther. This pattern of change, described by Bellak (1) as "the third psychiatric revolution," is not a strictly psychiatric phenomenon but has occurred as part of a far broader pattern of cultural change.

History reveals that there have been many surges of excitement and momentary thrusts in nearly every field of human endeavor (8). This pattern is clearly evident in psychiatry in both its negative phases, such as the persecution of demonic witches, and its positive phases, such as the moralistic and humanistic advances in hospital psychiatry in the United States in the mid-nineteenth century. Psychiatry has had its eras of institutional confinement in irons, "moral" therapy, massive institutional custodial care, and psychoanalytic predominance, and the emphasis now is on community psychiatry. The modern idea of humanitarian care is similar to that of the ancient Greeks (7) and to the enlightened concepts of over a century ago. Current psychiatric emphasis is on prevention of mental illness, early case-finding and diagnosis, and treatment of acute mental disorders in general hospitals or professional offices in the local community. Rehabilitation of the chronically mentally ill and provision for aftercare in a continuum of services within the community are other aspects of enlightened clinical psychiatric practice. The psychiatrist, however, is called upon to perform a variety of roles and his residency training has frequently left him ill prepared for some of them. He may now be serving as the responsible head of a community agency known as a "comprehensive community mental health center." Broad outlines have been given elsewhere of the functions of such an agency, in which a continuum of service is provided (10).

The present-day community psychiatrist may be expected to fulfill the roles of clinician (with psychiatric inpatients and outpatients and in semiresidential facilities), researcher, public and professional educator, administrator, supervisor, consultant, and community organizer, and to maintain complex interrelationships with a wide range of persons, agencies, and institutions in the community. He may need to assume responsibility for the mental health, present and future, of a number of persons in a catchment area related to the organization for which he works. Monitoring the mental health of that population, determining its mental health needs, and establishing resources to meet those needs may comprise some of his function. Caplan (2) has outlined the preventive aspects of his work, and responsibility for furthering "positive mental health," as described by Jahoda (5), may complicate his responsibilities still more.

Crests of humanistic advance have unfortunately failed to be sustained and have been followed by troughs when progress has been abandoned. Community psychiatry now stands astride one of those crests, which carries with it a surge of enthusiasm and excitement. However, many professionals in the mental health field and a skeptical public view it with mixed emotions, and rightly so. It is an area where monetary support flows relatively freely at all levels of government, and some will opportunistically use this support for persons and programs so tangential to community psychiatry that they actually detract from it.

Others decry community psychiatry as only one in a perpetual series of movements of high expectation that fail to achieve their goals. Some raise an outcry about its impact on traditional practices of clinical psychiatry, its concern with mass population and its socialistic leanings, its diffusion of professional role boundaries, its effects on human liberty and individualism, and the narrowness of its scientific base. None of these criticisms should be dismissed as invalid, for they deserve serious scrutiny.

Before we can deal with these areas, there must be some consensus as to what community psychiatry is. Some believe it is a meaningless collection of euphemisms, promises, and expectations. Others see it as the comprehensive clinical practice of psychiatry in the community that many highly trained, dynamic psychiatrists have been carrying on for a long time. Still others believe that community psychiatry encompasses all that a psychiatrist does outside the realm of traditional psychiatric inpatient and outpatient care. Another view envisions all community mental health activities, by lay or professional people, as residing within the province of community psychiatry.

I have defined community psychiatry as "a subspecialty of psychiatry, focusing on the prevention, diagnosis, treatment and rehabilitation of emotional illness and its sequelae in a given population" (8). There are a number of key words in this definition, but the most crucial is "population." Though the activities in this field must, and should, be constantly concerned with individual sufferers, the focus is on the given population. "Mental disorder" is a term preferable to "mental illness or disease," or "emotional illness or disease." In practical usage it may be possible, though difficult, to define consensually mental disorder with respect to given individuals, but we are far from determining the over-all boundary limits of mental disorder in a population. This stems partially from the psychiatrist's twofold concern with patterns of clinical distress or traditional psychiatric symptoms and the quite different, though overlapping, area of human maladaptation and disability. It is in the sphere of population that many people fail to understand what community psychiatry means. Specifically, it means that the psychiatrist, his staff, and his agency make the treatment of mental disorder in a given, defined community their responsibility. They are responsible for prevention of new cases, diagnosis and treatment of new and old cases, and rehabilitation of old cases. "Community" usually refers to a specified population, which may be contained within geographic boundaries, be related by common functional role or activity, or possess some common feature that defines it as a unit. The population contained within a geographically bounded area is a common unit of responsibility, though the community psychiatrist may work with a population delimited in other ways—for example, a group of persons with a common social system.

A useful conceptual model for community psychiatry is the public health model of prevention which Caplan elaborates (3). The key word here is "prevention," and three types of prevention in this model are germane to the concept of community. Primary prevention consists of measures to reduce the incidence of mental disorder in a community, that is, to lower the rate of occurrence of new cases per unit of population of risk during a designated period of time. It does not apply to specific individuals, each of whom might be interchangeable in the total population, but to numbers of persons. Secondary prevention consists of measures to reduce the prevalence of mental disorder in a community, that is, to reduce the rate of occurrence of new and established cases of mental disorder per unit of population of risk at any particular point in time. Tertiary prevention consists of measures to reduce residual defects consequent to mental disorder in a community, that is, to lower the residual defect level of cases of mental disorder per unit of population of risk over a designated period of time. Whereas clinical psychiatry and rehabilitation essentially focus on individuals, community psychiatry, though dealing with individuals in the population of a community, focuses on the community.

Within the conceptual model, programs must be evolved that can serve preventive goals. These programs will frequently involve more than one segment of the conceptual model, but each should be designed to meet a particular goal in a community psychiatry program, rather than to fit the model. The effectiveness of techniques for preventing new cases is largely unproven, though some programing, with outcome studies, is underway in this area. The methodological difficulties involved in conducting such research need no elaboration here.

A wide range of mental health professionals, agencies, and institutions have long been engaged in the diagnosis and treatment of mental disorders in the private, voluntary, and public sectors of the mental illness field. However, the poor co-ordination and gross unevenness of their dispersal among urban and rural regions and their quantitative inadequacy have usually resulted in far less than optimal care of the mentally ill. Comprehensive community mental health centers, which are only now coming into being in accordance with federal guidelines, are relatively recent additions to those facilities. It remains unclear how extensively, in practice, these facilities will develop psychiatric programs with a community focus. Each center will have a designated catchment area with a population of manageable size, but the nature of the program in operation and the agency professional staff will ultimately determine the center's ability to fulfill the hopes of the planners.

Though rehabilitation has become a fashionable area of professional activity, there has not been a great deal of work related to tertiary prevention. This is a relatively new concept in psychiatry with a community population focus. The combination of these varied types of programs in a single administrative or organizational unit has seldom been attempted in any comprehensive manner. It is hoped that this, along with training and research, may be achieved by the community psychiatrist in the programs under his administration. The activities of many professionals, some of them expert in areas in which the psychiatrist is significantly deficient, will be involved in this endeavor. Professional role boundaries are likely to be blurred in many programs as professionals engage in multiple functions.

What lies outside the boundaries of community psychiatry is even less well defined than the outer limits of the field. Some would include all human affairs within the borders of community psychiatric practice, since all man's activities are relevant to his present and future mental health. Some limit is placed through reference to community psychiatry as applicable to a given population. Within our definition, all social, psychological, and biological activity affecting the mental health of the populace is of interest to the community psychiatrist, including programs for fostering social change, resolution of social problems, political involvement, community organization planning, and clinical psychiatric practice.

Some of the models of community psychiatric practice in this volume outline the area of responsibility, clinical and otherwise, assumed by the community psychiatrist. Dr. Whittington describes his state level responsibility; Dr. Coburn discusses his work in a Canadian province with a population of one million; and Dr. Barnes presents a model of community psychiatry in a metropolitan area. Each defines through his own program his conception of the area of community psychiatry. A variety of other models could be presented to illustrate the definition of community psychiatry (4). However, those areas that lie outside the realm of community psychiatry would not be much better amplified by citing other current models.

Professor Kahn has coped with a definition of the boundary areas of community psychiatry. Resistance to the development of programs of community psychiatry is discussed by Dr. Rome. The theoretical basis for community psychiatry, which is essential to the comprehension and evolution of the field, is discussed by Dr. Sabshin. Professor Mechanic discusses the need to redefine the role of psychiatry in society in relation to some sociological implications. Professor Loeb deals with the central theme of the symposium in seeking a definition of community psychiatry.

Residency training programs are striving to incorporate into their curricula and fields of experience the body of knowledge and skills included in community psychiatry. The clinical service needs of psychiatric patients, the problem of the professional identity of the psychiatric resident, and the placement of additional material in an already crowded program of residency training complicate proposed alterations in these programs. Some of these issues are investigated by Drs. Zwerling and Rosenbaum. Dr. Wing reviews research in the United Kingdom in the community psychiatric area of care of schizophrenic patients. Professor Allen discusses legal aspects of community psychiatry.

In the continuing evolution of techniques, theory, and knowledge in psychiatry, the critic plays a crucial role. Dr. Halleck, as have others, assumes a critical stance in viewing present movement in the direction of community psychiatry (9). A review of our present position in the field is presented by Dr. Miller in an epilogue.

This book has not attempted to define related terms such as "social psychiatry," which has perhaps been even more loosely handled than "community psychiatry." Nor have many distinctions been made between the field of community psychiatry and the activities of the community psychiatrist. The future will, I am confident, provide us with a clearer definition of community psychiatry.

References

1 BELLAK, L. "Community Psychiatry: The Third Psychiatric Revolution." In *Handbook of Community Psychiatry and Community Mental Health,* edited by Leopold Bellak. New York, Grune & Stratton, 1964, p. 1.

2 CAPLAN, G. *An Approach to Community Mental Health.* New York, Grune & Stratton, 1961.

3 CAPLAN, G. *Principles of Preventive Psychiatry.* New York, Basic Books, 1964.

4 GLASSCOTE, R., SANDERS, D., FORSTENZER, H. M., AND FOLEY, A. R. *The Community Mental Health Center.* Washington, D.C., American Psychiatric Association and the National Association for Mental Health, 1964.

5 JAHODA, M. *Current Concepts of Positive Mental Health.* New York, Basic Books, 1958.
6 JOINT COMMISSION ON MENTAL ILLNESS AND HEALTH. *Action for Mental Health.* New York, Basic Books, 1961.
7 MASSERMAN, J. *The Practice of Dynamic Psychiatry.* Philadelphia, W. B. Saunders, 1955, p. 364.
8 ROBERTS, L. M. Expanding role of the psychiatrist in the community. *Diseases of the Nervous System* 26:147, 1965.
9 SZASZ, T. S. *Law, Liberty and Psychiatry.* New York, Macmillan, 1963.
10 U.S. PUBLIC HEALTH SERVICE. *Mental Health Activities and the Development of Comprehensive Health Programs in the Community.* Washington, D.C., 1962.

I

COMMUNITY
PSYCHIATRY
AND
SOCIAL
VALUES

One

Theoretical Models in Community and Social Psychiatry

MELVIN SABSHIN, M.D.

J UXTAPOSING the words "theory" and "community psychiatry" may appear hopelessly paradoxical, for community psychiatry undoubtedly conveys to many an image of long overdue action, of meeting social responsibility, and of departing the ivory or aluminum tower for the real world. To some the image may be just as pragmatic but tainted by professional grandiosity and political chicanery. These images, whether pro or con, have a distinctly American flavor, not surprising since community psychiatry in this mid-decade is strikingly typical of our national attempts at massive and occasionally restless solutions of social problems. The action-oriented viewpoint is so pervasive that a discussion of theory may seem to be merely a delaying tactic. Having had some experience with pragmatic community psychiatrists and their equally action-oriented detractors, I wish to avoid sounding like a history professor addressing a national political convention, just before the first balloting, on the relationships of de Tocqueville and Jefferson as they pertain to candidate selection. Community psychiatry is like a swirling modern convention blaring with noise and spirit that is being beamed to large numbers of friends and neutrals and the opposition party. Bellak hails it as "the third psychiatric revolution" in his new book (*1*). Dunham

(5), clearly alarmed, calls it "the newest therapeutic band-wagon," and a hundred other slogans are in the process of being manufactured as the anti-community psychiatry groups begin to notice each other. It is painful for psychiatrists to accept how much of our activity reflects segmentalized ideological positions or can be characterized as a "movement" in the sense that Freud uses the term in "The History of the Psychoanalytic Movement" (10). In a recent paper (6) and in a forthcoming book (22), several colleagues and I have summarized our own studies of psychiatric ideologies and institutions. The overwhelming major-ity of the four hundred psychiatrists studied considered them-selves to be reasonably and broadly eclectic, even though their questionnaire scores and, more important, their behavior often indicated strongly partisan positions. The readiness to accept or dismiss community psychiatry seems as closely related to these partisan stands as to any other factor, although to my knowledge this relationship has not yet been investigated. The progress of community psychiatry is hampered by interprofessional jurisdic-tional issues as well as intraprofessional concerns. Sociologists, social workers, social psychologists, and public health experts have raised serious questions regarding the psychiatrist's fitness for leading community psychiatry or community mental health programs. The level of alarm rises precipitously when the lan-guage employed by the psychiatrist suggests treatment of a collectivity in a massive experiment in social engineering. Impli-cations have been seen in these suggestions of everything from the threat of a society regimented in an Orwellian fashion to a communist or an extreme rightist plot. That community psy-chiatry has been able to develop despite these divergent opinions, conflicting perspectives, and sinister implications is, in my opin-ion, largely a result of the enormity of unmet mental health needs and the determined, though awkward, effort of a group of professions to realign themselves so as to meet these needs. The social reorganization of many of our psychiatric hospitals in the 1950's, the report of the Joint Commission on Mental Illness and Health (14), and the late President's now historic message on mental health have paved the way, and the time is now propitious for such a realignment.

This is not the first time in the twentieth century that the United States has seemed ready for a community approach. The period antedating the flowering of the child guidance movement in the 1920's also saw the enthusiastic entry of the mental health professions into the wider area of social process. The pioneering efforts of Healy, Bronner, Levy, and others marked the birth of child psychiatry, and the city of Chicago played a prominent part in the early nurturence of this field in the halcyon days at the Institute for Juvenile Research. Healy's deep interest in problems of delinquency led him and his colleagues out of the consulting rooms and into the arena of public action. From this arena ultimately evolved the child guidance clinics and the search for a preventive approach. It is not surprising that some of the older generation of child psychiatrists view the current trends in community psychiatry as a repetition of days gone by. During the course of a half-century, however, the child guidance movement gradually lost the momentum of its preventive approach and, at least until quite recently, also lost its major commitment to a community perspective. This loss of momentum was primarily a result of too much emphasis on pragmatics and too little emphasis on research. The lessons for community psychiatry today are patent.

This conference, as its title indicates, is devoted to defining community psychiatry. But other terms and labels will be used which may be hard to distinguish from community psychiatry: social psychiatry, comprehensive psychiatry, community mental health, preventive psychiatry, administrative psychiatry, public health psychiatry, community organization, community planning. The possibility of placing adjectives before the word "psychiatry" seems to be infinite. Stephen E. Goldston of the Training and Manpower Resources Branch of the National Institute of Mental Health has recently compiled a list of selected definitions (11) of terms related to community psychiatry which is useful in appreciating the complexity of the perspectives on this field. I will limit my own definitions to the areas of social psychiatry and community psychiatry. The framework within which these definitions will be formulated is certainly not unique, but I believe that it differs from others at least in its emphasis on and possible usefulness for theory and research. Since my conceptual model of community psychiatry involves its being subsumed under social psychiatry, I shall first discuss social psychiatry, then define community psychiatry, and, finally, attempt to weave them together.

In a previous paper (*18*) outlining the historical evolution of social psychiatry, I have traced its roots in broad, ameliorative movements. In Germany after World War I, for example, there was a sudden burst of interest in social psychiatry. As Dreikurs (*4*) has indicated, textbooks of social psychiatry appeared, and psychiatrists worked in courts, schools, and government much as did Healy and his collaborators in this country. Ten years later German social psychiatry came to a sudden halt with the rise of Naziism. Leighton (*16*) has pointed out that social psychiatry has somewhat different meanings in America and abroad, particularly in England. He states, "In the United States the term usually brings to mind preventive community programs, industrial and forensic psychiatry, group therapy, and participation of psychiatry in administrative medicine, the utilization of the social milieu in treatment, and the study of social factors in the etiology and dynamics of mental illness. In England, social psychiatry is more likely to connote an emphasis on social amelioration as reflected in the development of various treatment services; it has been less closely related to general developments in the social sciences." In the United States, however, social psychiatry is coming increasingly to connote a demarcated theoretical and research area. Redlich and Pepper (*17*), for example, have stated, "Our own brief definition, influenced by Rennie, defines social psychiatry as the study of psychiatric disorders and psychiatric therapy, hopefully including prevention, within a social setting. This implies that social psychiatry is defined as an exploration of social systems and culture and their impact on psychiatric phenomena rather than as a type of psychiatric practice." Redlich and Pepper's emphasis is on study and exploration; Wilmer, on the other hand, emphasizes a pattern of psychiatric practice in the first part of his description of social psychiatry (*23*): "an area where physicians qualified as trained psychiatrists . . . utilize selective contributions of social psychology, medicine, and psychiatry in the prevention and treatment of emotional and mental illness; in the rehabilitation, socialization, and acculturation of the sick from any cause whatsoever." Wilmer (23) goes on to include theoretical aspects when he states that social psychiatry is also involved "in the scientific study of etiologies, hypotheses, theories, and treatment concepts under field or operating conditions. . . ." Similarly, Harris (11) has defined social psychiatry as "that part of psychiatry concerned with various aspects of society as it relates to emotional disturbance. Insofar as it is similar to social psychology, its emphasis is probably more theoretical than practical." My own definition essentially concurs with that of Harris but goes beyond it at least in one specific sense. I have defined social psychiatry (18) as an emergent theoretical and research field in which sophisticated employment of both social science and psychiatric variables is necessary for understanding a problem and, ultimately, for finding medically useful solutions to it. By "sophisticated" I mean that the independent and dependent variables, whether they stem from social science or from psychiatry, will be based on mature, professional understanding of both areas; and by "emergent," that the social psychiatry of the future should become increasingly sophisticated in developing interactional and transactional models and hypotheses. Most current studies employ a simple interactional design in which attempts are made to correlate social and psychiatric phenomena. Hollingshead and Redlich's study (12) of the interaction of social stratification and diagnostic categorization of psychiatric patients is prototypic of current social psychiatric research. Not only does it represent an interactional, rather than a transactional, model, but the independent social variables and the dependent psychiatric variables, though adequate, are vulnerable to criticism since they lack specificity or precision. Studies in the area of social class and mental illness should, in the future, become more sophisticated and increasingly focused, and should move towards predictive statements. Epidemiological studies will also require increasing precision to fit within my definition of social psychiatry. A repetition of Faris and Dunham's (7) pioneering effort in correlating gross residential locale in an urban context with the prevalence rates of specific psychoses would not, without refining the variables, constitute sophisticated social psychiatric research in the 1960's. The utilization of relatively unsophisticated experimental design in studying the dependent variables should also be increasingly questioned. Sociologists have frequently tended to be somewhat naive in their use of psychiatric dependent variables, just as psychiatrists have occasionally been slipshod in their use of cultural and social variables. One excellent illustration of the latter has been the search for anthropological evidence to support a particular psychiatric hypothesis. The mourning process as formulated by psychiatrists is often assumed to possess essentially universalistic characteristics. Transcultural evidence has been utilized to support this postulation, but there has been little interest in broadening or altering the basic hypothesis to take into account dependent cultural variables that do not conform to the original hypothesis. Hospital psychiatry affords us a number of excellent examples of good social psychiatric research. That studies on the interaction of social milieu and process or outcome of therapy are becoming increasingly sophisticated is evidenced by recent efforts to develop more complex transactional designs (15). My definition of social psychiatry is obviously quite close to some of the earlier definitions of social psychology. Social psychiatry is encountering some of the same problems that social psychology experienced in its early years, but I would predict that social psychiatry, like social psychology, will become increasingly specific. Although I have emphasized the theoretical and research aspects of social psychiatry, I believe that it differs from social psychology in all of the issues determining the differences between psychiatry and psychology. Thus, social psychiatry is slightly more pragmatic than social psychology and necessarily maintains ties with many applied areas.

One of the most unfortunate consequences of the division of psychiatrists into various ideological subgroupings involves the fact that the advent of social psychiatry posed new dilemmas for psychiatrists oriented toward somatotherapy and psychotherapy. The social psychiatrists who speak as if the human beings were born with a *tabula rasa,* and who view therapy exclusively within a framework of altering social structure, readily lend themselves to criticism, most notably and visibly today from the psychoanalysts. The relationship between social psychiatry and psychoanalysis affords an excellent example of the dangers of conflicting sectarian approaches. Extremists in social psychiatry and psychoanalysis view each other with marked suspicion. Some social and community psychiatrists hold psychoanalysis largely responsible for moving American psychiatry out of the mainstream of its responsibilities for the care of those with major mental illnesses. A few psychoanalysts, on the other hand, have become concerned and even suspicious about the tendency of social psychiatrists to dilute or, if you will, inundate the intrapsychic with the cultural and the social. Several psychoanalysts involved in training psychiatric residents have repeatedly pointed out that trainees can utilize social process as a defense against involvement with patients and hence as a device to avoid commitment to therapeutic endeavors. Many psychoanalysts are guarded about the present role of social science in psychiatry because they tend to equate undue interest on the social level with so-called "revisionism" in psychoanalysis. It is my conviction, however, that a sophisticated social psychiatry that avoids the cul-de-sac of a *tabula rasa* model and attempts to provide meaningful links between social process and psychological events has no essential disagreement with the science of psychoanalysis. It also has no basic quarrel with the biological aspects of mental health and illness. I have attempted in one study (19) to correlate aspects of the social setting with response to psychopharmacological agents; in another (20) I have tried to demonstrate how a number of parameters in the social setting affected psychophysiological variables in the psychosomatic laboratory. Illustrations could be cited to demonstrate the application of the social psychiatric perspective to an array of psychiatric problems, issues, and settings. Clearly, social psychiatry as I have defined it is also pertinent to the study of group process; it provides an organizational framework for approaches to family diagnosis and therapy; it is relevant for the recently revived field of transcultural psychiatry; and it provides, as well, a broader theoretical perspective from which to view both hospital and community psychiatry. It is somewhat paradoxical that friction exists between advocates of hospital psychiatry and those in community mental health programs since both, it seems to me, rely heavily on social psychiatric theory. It is impossible to practice good hospital psychiatry today without paying attention to both the broad and the specific impacts of the milieu on the diagnostic and treatment processes, just as it is impossible to be a community psychiatrist without taking a serious interest in both the particularities of the community and their impact on those who live in it. Obviously, most of the friction comes from polar groups who either view with alarm the rapid dissolution of the large state hospitals or are impatient with progress in increasing the permeability between hospital and community. The interaction of the hospital and community approaches is analogous to the relationship of social psychiatry and psychoanalysis, which have much more in common than they have in opposition and are clearly related not only in their links with social psychiatry but in their functional interaction. This is most evident in situations where community psychiatry is centered about a multipurpose institute that provides not only inpatient and transitional services (such as day hospital and halfway houses) but home visits and clinic care. Furthermore, many research linkages exist between community and hospital psychiatry. Comparative analyses of the impact of various aspects of therapeutic services, for example, have already proven useful. It is to be hoped that this kind of research will increase in both scope and breadth.

In describing the relationship of social psychiatry and community psychiatry, I have indicated a model in which a general research field (social psychiatry) is related to one of its subparts (community psychiatry) which, though it has specific functions, is not merely an applied area. Before this model is elaborated, an alternative viewpoint should be considered. In discussing community psychiatry, one of its most experienced practitioners, Viola Bernard (2), has stated, "Community psychiatry and social psychiatry are often used interchangeably and we believe with considerable justification. We recognize many areas of overlap between the two. However, in distinguishing between them, we think that community psychiatry tends to signify a greater emphasis on applied practice at the community level, as well as the investigations and program evaluations which underlie and keep shaping its service operations, while social psychiatry has come to connote a more exclusive emphasis on theory and research rather than practice. Therefore, community psychiatry in encompassing both is viewed as the more comprehensive designation." While I agree with Bernard that social psychiatry places greater emphasis on theory and research and that community psychiatry must involve service operations, I cannot agree that community psychiatry, in encompassing both theory and practice, is the more comprehensive designation. Such a view, I believe, is not only contrary to our usual distinctions between the more basic areas and the applied areas but tends to weaken the argument for social psychiatry's central position in relation to a number of other areas, such as hospital psychiatry. My conceptual model views social psychiatry as a sun with a number of planets in orbit around it. Each of the planets interacts with the others as well as with the sun. While Bernard is careful not to imply, as others have done, that community psychiatry is only an applied area and that social psychiatry is its theoretical source, she places greater emphasis on an applied definition of community psychiatry than I find optimal. The pragmatic model of community psychiatry has a number of weaknesses. In discussing the child guidance movement I described the ultimate weakening of an area oversaturated with faith, hope, and enthusiasm. If community psychiatry becomes an applied field exclusively, it may well not live up to its promise. One danger is that the applied model may tend to attract less capable individuals than a model that offers theoretical generativity as well as exciting service opportunities. In a paper presented recently to a conference on training in community psychiatry, I stated that (21): "What we need most is to attract first-class individuals to community psychiatry, including those who will become the models for future trainees." I went on to emphasize that our very best trainees will be excited and intrigued by a new idea, but that they can make no long-term commitment to a field that, though full of action, lacks substance. Community psychiatry could not, under such circumstances, compete with other aspects of psychiatry, and it must compete in the professional market place for the available talent. My emphasis has been misinterpreted if I appear to be saying that community psychiatry should not have a service base. On the contrary, community psychiatry cannot exist without such a base, but the pendulum has moved much too far in that direction.

Community psychiatry, as I would define it, involves the utilization of the techniques, methods, and theories of social psychiatry and other behavioral sciences to investigate and to meet the mental health needs of a functionally or geographically defined population over a significant period of time, and the feeding back of information to modify the central body of social psychiatric and other behavioral science knowledge. Part of this statement is borrowed from Caplan (3), who has essentially defined community psychiatry as the process of meeting the mental health needs of a functionally or geographically defined population. While Caplan is deeply committed to the evolution of theoretical models in community psychiatry and has contributed as much to such models as any psychiatrist, his definition places insufficient stress on a feedback system in which social psychiatric concepts and methods can be brought into play and, consequently, significantly affected by community psychiatry. Duhl's definition also lacks emphasis on the rich research possibilities of community psychiatry. Duhl (11) defines community psychiatry as "concern with optimizing the adaptive potential and psychosocial life skills as well as lessening the amount of pathology in population groups (communities, functional groups, etc.) by population-wide programs of prevention, case-finding, care, treatment, and rehabilitation. The individual becomes important not only as an individual problem but also as a flag of a more general psychiatric need of a population group." Like Caplan, Duhl has been influenced by the public health model of community psychiatry. While both Caplan and Duhl are exceedingly broad in vision and scope, their public health model seems to imply that the major task of community psychiatry involves the ready-made application of models of primary, secondary, and tertiary prevention. I agree wholeheartedly that this is an important part of community psychiatry, but I take issue with those who equate community psychiatry exclusively with a public health preventive approach. Hume, for example, states (13), "Community psychiatry does not take positive mental health as its focus. Rather the focus of community psychiatry is upon prevention." I object to the rigidity inherent in this limitation of community psychiatry, and to the resulting difficulty of generating alternative models. I also object to a model that does not recognize community psychiatry's emergence as an area devoted to the formulation of new hypotheses.

A community center jointly developed by the Chicago Board of Health, the Illinois Department of Mental Health, and the University of Illinois department of psychiatry is an example of a program in community psychiatry committed equally to service and to research. Although the center has been in operation for less than a year, it has already been responsible for a number of interesting developments. The area within which the center functions is a classic example of the geographically defined community model. It is a section on the south side of Chicago called Woodlawn, whose 82,000 inhabitants, of whom almost 100 per cent are Negro, live within a clear-cut geographic boundary. Woodlawn's population is not homogenous but falls into two general categories: a stable, home-owning, middle-class population that resides in the western area; and a complex concatenation of groups that reside, in some instances in slum areas, in the east. Leadership at the center is provided by three psychiatrists, all of whom have moved to Chicago within the past year and hold appointments in the university department of psychiatry where they are now providing significant leadership in training. The center itself is located in an office building in a densely populated part of Woodlawn. It consists of a suite of comfortable offices, conference rooms, waiting rooms, and secretarial space. It was apparent from its very inception, however, that the center would not and could not be a traditional psychiatric clinic. Instead, it has undertaken to provide consultative services to a broad network of agencies within the area. It has now passed through the first stage of entry into the community. Progress has occasionally been stormy, but a viable dialogue has developed with broad segments of the community's leadership and a strong advisory committee has been drawn from the Woodlawn area to provide local sanction. Contact has been established with legal agencies, religious groups, school officials, social agencies, physicians, neighborhood clubs and organizations, recreational groups, and the major political groups within the geographic boundaries. Meetings with these groups have resulted in frank discussions about the community's fears and expectations of the psychiatrists' role, and a number of stereotypes have been at least partially erased. The dialogue has not been a one-way process; we have received even more of an education than we have provided.

While it has been clearly recognized that the development of service operations is of paramount importance, center leadership has undertaken the difficult and ambitious project of working out sanctions to give strong emphasis to research operations. While this task has still to be completed, close ties with a department of psychiatry afford a medium for its successful accomplishment. The directors of the center * are also engaged in delineating research proposals that promise to aid the service functions. They are now developing, for example, a plan to study the way teachers tag first grade students as emotionally disturbed. Following the social psychiatric perspective, they are interested in the teachers who do the tagging and the setting in which they make their decisions. Not only the ecological characteristics of tagged and untagged children, but the very process of tagging, requires study. Obviously, the psychological status of the children must also be carefully investigated, and psychiatrically sophisticated instruments have been developed for this purpose. The second step in this research will involve following up the tagged students and comparing them with an adequate control group. Intervention of various types, including attempts at changing the setting, the teachers, the family, and the children, will then be utilized to ascertain which, if any, of these interventions may alter the deleterious consequences of being or becoming a child labeled as emotionally disturbed. The group at the center has also studied broad epidemiological and ecological characteristics of individuals requiring psychiatric hospitalization, and of Woodlawn adolescents classified as delinquents. These epidemiological surveys are rich in implications for social psychiatric theory and are useful, as well, in developing guidelines for services such as

* Drs. Sheldon Schiff, Sheppard Kellam, and Edward Futterman.

providing aid for citizens who require full or partial hospitalization. The group at the Woodlawn center has also been deeply
interested in the process by which the community defines deviance or mental illness. A number of social agencies in the
Woodlawn area have their own definitions of deviant behavior.
The welfare department, for example, has developed a special list
of people receiving aid because of what the department feels are
clear-cut psychological problems. The police have also classified
various types of psychological deviation, and center personnel
were surprised at the amount of relevant behavioral data the
police had obtained.

The issue of the community's definition of deviance, illness,
and health touches on one of psychiatry's central theoretical and
research problems: the development of an adequate theoretical
model for defining mental health. Psychiatry lags behind several
other medical disciplines in possession of adequate samples of
nomothetic and of normative data. Although concepts of mental
health and illness have clearly been correlated with current forms
of psychiatric practice, we have lacked the practical means as
well as adequate models for establishing what is healthy. At the
turn of the century, when psychiatry was essentially a hospital
specialty, it was fairly simple to be concerned only with cases of
gross psychopathology and to assume that the remaining 99 per
cent of the population were mentally healthy, since health was
defined as the antonym of gross psychopathology. Psychoanalysis
changed this concept considerably. Freud thought of normality or
health as an "ideal fiction" (9). Not all analysts agree with
Freud's concept, but it is apparent that psychoanalysis has not
been able to develop a convincing theory of mental health. With a
few significant exceptions, psychoanalysts have not been deeply
interested in empirical normative studies, especially studies of
adult populations. One of the reasons that the collection of
normative data on adult populations has not developed into a
major research concern has been the implicit assumptions that the
population seen by the psychoanalyst is a representative sample,
and that the range of behavior seen in psychoanalytic practice is a
good cross-section of the type of clinical problems existing in the
various strata of American life. In my opinion, the bulk of the

evidence goes in the other direction. Psychoanalysis has studied a limited segment of the American population, and what is needed now is the collection of empirical data, by psychoanalysts as well as others, on populations who do not come to our offices. Community psychiatry is in a unique position to provide such data. I do not mean data that merely echo our current theoretical models. Epidemiological studies that report a very high percentage of psychiatric disease in any particular population probably reflect the lack of clarity in our conceptualization of health and illness. We need new tools, new concepts, and new observations of individuals in new settings. Functionally as well as geographically organized community psychiatric centers will help fulfill this need. Psychiatrists are moving in increasing numbers to functionally defined communities, which may vary from a group of small industries to a group of labor unions interested in their community's mental health needs. Studies might involve the mental health needs of members of the Peace Corps, American Indians moved from the reservation, or students attending a university. Psychiatrists working in collegiate health programs have a unique opportunity to study the interaction of the collegiate milieu and the problems it creates or fails to create or ameliorate in the adolescents who pass through its doors. Social psychiatric studies such as these (8) have contributed and may contribute further to our knowledge of both psychopathology and normal coping mechanisms.

The mental health center sponsored by the University of Illinois represents only one possibility for the development of a community psychiatric program. It is to be hoped that there will be considerable heterogeneity in the evolution of these programs, so that comparative analysis will become both possible and feasible. If the Montefiore Hospital in New York City is able to achieve its goal of serving the census tract surrounding it, it can make a unique contribution to community psychiatry. A family court may be an ideal setting for the development of a community psychiatric program. In Massachusetts a number of such court centers have been developed where the leadership is not only sophisticated about psychiatric phenomena but also knowledgeable about family law and the complexities of the court setting. Each of these types of community mental health centers has unique problems as well as unique opportunities to broaden our knowledge about etiology and treatment.

It is relatively simple to advocate the evolution of theoretical models; it is quite another thing to develop new models in actuality. What I have attempted here is to indicate the directions that development of a new model of community psychiatry should take. Psychiatry has entered a new phase of realignment within the social fabric of our culture, and the tasks this entails cannot be accomplished without meaningful collaboration with other disciplines. Community psychiatry and social psychiatry are far too broad in scope to be limited to the confines of a single discipline. In moving toward these new directions we must, of course, be prepared to take risks, but there are limits to risk taking, and reasonable boundaries must be established. In the long run I am convinced that the clarifications and definitions we now lack will be provided by a new generation of investigators and clinicians who will have been stimulated to enter community psychiatry if our generation helps to make it an exciting field.

References

1 BELLAK, LEOPOLD, ED. Handbook of Community Psychiatry and Community Mental Health. New York, Grune & Stratton, 1964.

2 BERNARD, VIOLA W. "Education for Community Psychiatry in a University Medical Center." In Handbook of Community Psychiatry and Community Mental Health, edited by Leopold Bellak. New York, Grune & Stratton, 1964, pp. 82–123.

3 CAPLAN, GERALD. "Community Psychiatry—Introduction and Overview." In Concepts of Community Psychiatry, edited by Stephen E. Goldston. Washington, D.C., U.S. Dept. of Health, Education, and Welfare, 1965, pp. 3–18.

4 DREIKURS, RUDOLF. Early experiments in social psychiatry. Int. J. soc. Psychiat. 7:141–47, 1961.

5 DUNHAM, H. W. Community psychiatry: The newest therapeutic bandwagon. A.M.A. Arch. Gen. Psychiat. 12:303–13, 1965.

6 EHRLICH, D., AND SABSHIN, M. A study of sociotherapeutically oriented psychiatrists. Amer. J. Orthopsychiat. 34:469–80, 1964.

7 FARIS, ROBERT E. L., AND DUNHAM, H. W. Mental Disorders in Urban Areas. Chicago, Univ. of Chicago Press, 1939.

8 FARNSWORTH, DANA L. Mental Health in College and University. Cambridge, Harvard Univ. Press, 1957.

9 FREUD, SIGMUND. "Analysis Terminable and Interminable" (first published in 1937). *Collected Papers,* Vol. V, edited by Ernest Jones. London, The Hogarth Press, 1950, pp. 316–57.

10 FREUD, SIGMUND. "On the History of the Psychoanalytic Movement" (first published in 1914). *Collected Papers,* Vol. I, edited by Ernest Jones. London, The Hogarth Press, 1949, pp. 287–359.

11 GOLDSTON, STEPHEN E. "Selected Definitions." In *Concepts of Community Psychiatry,* edited by Stephen E. Goldston. Washington, D.C., U.S. Dept. of Health, Education, and Welfare, 1965, pp. 195–204.

12 HOLLINGSHEAD, A. B., AND REDLICH, F. C. *Social Class and Mental Illness.* New York, Wiley, 1958.

13 HUME, PORTIA B. "Principles and Practice of Community Psychiatry: The Role and Training of the Specialist in Community Psychiatry." In *Handbook of Community Psychiatry and Community Mental Health,* edited by Leopold Bellak. New York, Grune & Stratton, 1964, pp. 65–82.

14 JOINT COMMISSION ON MENTAL ILLNESS AND HEALTH. *Action for Mental Health.* New York, Basic Books, 1961.

15 KELLAM, SHEPPARD T., DURELL, JACK, AND SHADER, RICHARD. Measurement of staff attitudes and the clinical course of patients on a psychiatric ward. Paper presented at a meeting of The Association for the Advancement of Psychotherapy, Los Angeles, California, May 3, 1964.

16 LEIGHTON, ALEXANDER H. *My Name Is Legion.* New York, Basic Books, 1959.

17 REDLICH, F. C., AND PEPPER, MAX P. Social psychiatry. *Amer. J. Psychiat. 116:*611–16, 1960.

18 SABSHIN, MELVIN. Current perspectives in social psychiatry. Paper presented before the Illinois Psychiatric Society, Chicago, Illinois, April 18, 1962.

19 SABSHIN, MELVIN, AND EISEN, SYDNEY B. The effects of ward tension on the quality and quantity of tranquilizer utilization. *Ann. N.Y. Acad. Sci. 67:*746–56, 1957.

20 SABSHIN, MELVIN, *et al.* Significance of pre-experimental studies in the psychosomatic laboratory. *A.M.A. Arch. Neurol. Psychiat.* 78:207–19, 1957.

21 SABSHIN, MELVIN. "Theory and Practice of Community Psychiatry Training in the Medical School Setting." In *Concepts of Community Psychiatry,* edited by Stephen E. Goldston. Washington, D.C., U.S. Dept. of Health, Education, and Welfare, 1965, pp. 49–56.

22 STRAUSS, A., SCHATZMAN, L., BUCHER, R., EHRLICH, D., AND SABSHIN, M. *Psychiatric Ideologies and Institutions.* New York, The Free Press of Glencoe, 1964.

23 WILMER, HARRY A. *Social Psychiatry in Action.* Springfield, Illinois, Thomas, 1958.

Two

Barriers to the Establishment of Comprehensive Community Mental Health Centers

HOWARD P. ROME, M.D.

R ESISTANCE is encountered in the diffusion of every innovation in a social system, and the difficulties involved in the
establishment of a community mental health program are compounded by factors that have come to be thought of almost as
elements of mental illness itself (*15*). Acting conjointly, these
factors create barriers to the provision in the community of the
kind of treatment for mental illness that is commonly available to
patients suffering from other kinds of disease.

Up to the time of the report of the Joint Commission on Mental
Illness and Health (*14*), the major emphasis of such inquiries was
on the psychological impediments to progress, an approach that
seemed to assume that psychological vagaries are idiosyncratic
phenomena rather than the expression of widely-held attitudes
and values. In contrast, this review of the problem will attempt to
formulate the issues in a broader context, and to view the so-
called barriers to the acceptance of a community mental health
program as blockages in a complex ecological interchange of
information.

At one pole is a system of culture values ostensibly dedicated to
the needs of the individual, as opposed to the needs of the

collectivity of which he is a member. This individualistic system of values has its own ethos, its mystique, and its myths; although it somewhat overstates its thesis, it assumes that man lives in opposition to society, and many of its theories incorporate this assumption. Man, in this context, is said to be antagonistic to social controls and resentful of paternalism, not only within the nuclear family but in society at large. The tenets of this system hold that by and large all men have to be treated as if they were equal. It is assumed that given minimal restraints, man is capable of getting what he needs and wants if he applies himself to the task. Failure to achieve is almost by definition prima-facie evidence of weakness, lack of nerve, and deficient initiative and motivation; of some crippling which makes one that much less of a man. In the face of such an admission of failure, a man loses his enfranchisement and thereby qualifies for charity or its euphemism, welfare. Having failed the means test in this sense, he is clearly entitled to subsistence benefits. These, however, should never equal what he would have had, had he earned it on his own. The rationalization for this marginal support seems to be that if a man were given as much as he might earn, it would deprive him of the moral incentive to which he must at least aspire.

The attitudinal set that typifies the individualistic culture has been variously labeled, but its most descriptive status-attribute is embodied in the term "frontier psychology." This concept, with its image of man alone, confronting his destiny, emphasizes the individual condition and views the environment, both natural and manmade, as a potentially hostile one from which the prudent and the resourceful must at all times be prepared to defend themselves.

There are, as Snow has pointed out, remediable and irremediable features of the human individual condition.* It is the recognition and separation of those which are intrinsic from those which can be remedied by techniques now known that are the preoccupation of persons concerned with the second culture, the social condition.

* C. P. Snow, *The Two Cultures: And a Second Look* (New York: Macmillan, 1964).

The attitude that glorifies the myth or stereotype of the frontiersman is based on certain unrealistic notions. Like his forebears in Western Europe whose penurious fate he chose to avoid, the frontiersman was in fact quite different from his descendants' view of him. He was a hungry man and more often than not a sick man. Most of his children died in infancy, and, more likely than not, an early death because of childbirth or because of one of the complications of pregnancy was the fate of his wife.

The confrontation and acceptance of these social and historical facts would represent a breach in the first barrier to planning for a community mental health center. To separate fact from myth requires detailed scrutiny of shifts in economic philosophy and analysis of dry statistics, demographic records, and various taxonomic indices of morbidity related to social class, income, and education as well as disease. Notions about health, like all other notions, are born of wishful thinking.

It seems fairly clear, however, that despite this undercurrent of rugged individualism governmental programs in education and health conservation, as well as in rehabilitation, have become basically Keynesian in their conceptualization. According to this thesis, it is a consequence of the nature of capitalistic economies that serious imbalances develop and that government is therefore required to influence national income and employment and affect social programs by manipulating their ingredients—that is, consumption, savings, and investment—as well as their determinants. Thus, of necessity, government is involved in monetary policy. It has a similar role in its fiscal relationships: it influences both total consumption and investment through policies such as taxation, welfare, and subsidies which affect income. Awards, grants, and subsidies affect the social structure by stressing set values and by influencing yield on investment and distribution of resources. Mental health matters also require political manipulation of the variables that indirectly affect supply and demand. The behavioral area, for example, is faced by the scarcity of skilled personnel, for in the community pool of professionals, the availability of commodity services is directly proportional to the remuneration that accrues in the process of rendering service.

In view of our society's strong tradition of economic individualism and government non-intervention, governmental involvement in economic and social life is bound to be viewed by many with distaste. However, the classical laissez-faire policy of the nineteenth century no longer operates. It is historical fact that the government, encouraged by the increasing need for co-ordination of political, economic, and social institutions, has intervened in such activities as direct assistance programs as well as in the promotion, management, regulation, operation, and manipulation of a great range of other economic and social activities. Government intervention has been justified, too, by the increasingly thorny problem of securing political and social justice in the face of shifting social tides. Certainly, the events of World War I, the Depression, World War II, and the Cold War call for a high level of collective mobilization of all our resources.

Needless to say, the issues here are clouded by strong feelings. To some, increasing governmental regulation and involvement do violence to the traditional American values of individualism, equality of opportunity and regional independence, the populist ideals that are the essence of the frontier spirit.

The technological advances that have occurred in medicine and its allied sciences have raised another significant barrier. With the exponential growth of scientific knowledge there necessarily has been specialization, which has meant fragmentation of interests as well as compartmentalization of services. The professionalization of these splinter interests has led to widespread social institutionalization of specialty disciplines within medicine which is antithetical to a comprehensive and integrated service (3). This professionalization process has its fratricidal aspects as well. While in some spheres the conflict is nominalistic, in others it is characterized by such tangible manifestations as professional disenfranchisement, economic sanctions, and coercive power moves. The factional differences resulting from specialization are based on allegiances among professional and subprofessional disciplines. In the field of mental health care, a major barrier has been created by the separation of psychiatry from medicine as a whole, a barrier fortified by the fact that the extra-medical needs of mental health clientele have demanded as well a separation from the traditional technology of medicine.

In varying degrees, all professions involve a commitment to standards of knowledge and excellence and a commitment to practice in accordance with these standards. When professionals enter bureaucracies, however, a conflict arises between their independent commitment to professional standards and ethics and their necessary involvement in the commercial or social interests of the bureaucracy. This gives rise to tensions and conflicts both within the organization and between organizations. There often develops, in addition, an ambiguous authority relationship between the experts of the staff and the managers of the line, and this is aggravated by the differences in their educational backgrounds and in their styles of professional life and practice. The mental health professional thus becomes a man-in-the-middle in an area of conflicting expectations and ambiguities. His identification is difficult and confusing. His status as a member of a bureaucracy—for example, as a physician in a state hospital—is distinctly lower than it would be if he were a solo entrepreneur.

A research unit affiliated with a comprehensive mental health center faces much the same problem: as a result of the affiliation, its research must be focal, relevant, specific, and directed, requirements which are said to be contradictory to the fundamental concept of open-shop research. This seems to be another aspect of the man-in-the-middle dilemma, a present-day role-problem not unlike the nineteenth-century problem of the exploited worker.

In contrast to the business firm as a classical example of an organization guided by the criterion of profit maximization, the behavior of a health organization is gauged by the demands for its product, by its capacity to maintain a varied supply of services, and by the scope of its operations as measured by the number of its clients and the professional status of its staff.

Mental health facilities have the socially assigned role of caring for what has been termed the "post-bankruptcy" experience of the family (24), a phenomenon that has to be understood in the light of the shifting role of the nuclear family in recent years. The family has as its central functions the socialization of the young and the provision of an outlet for expression of the emotions and tensions of family members; in modern society these are almost its only functions. Consequently, when, in effect, adverse forces render the family bankrupt in the capacity to discharge these functions properly, society resorts to contrived, substituted, institutional arrangements such as child labor laws, aid-to-dependent-children, adoption procedures, poor laws, insurance, charity, welfare funds, and psychiatric clinics to compensate for this insolvency. These institutional arrangements are designed to guarantee to families a floor of security and to lend them an element of stability. Psychiatry, as a medical specialty concerned with the vagaries of behavior, has been expected to assume the role of a scientific arbiter in representing society's interest in the expeditious solution of these matters. The division of opinion over the social philosophy on which this assumption is based, however, constitutes a major barrier to the provision of comprehensive services.

A socially determined variable in the economics of demand for services is the difference between the private practice of psychiatry and its public practice (5). Those who can afford it, and who have been educated to accept the value system that condones it, seek treatment for their personal expressions of anomia. The character of these patients is quite different from that of those whom society judges to be in need of control through treatment or custodial care. The former group views psychiatry more or less in the light of latter-day moralists; the latter reacts to the implications of externally imposed controls.

This dichotomous approach has cast all psychiatric treatment into one of these two diametrically opposed contexts. Psychoanalysis, for example, has a marked prestige value for certain social, educational, and economic segments of society. Because of the high demand for psychoanalysis and the short supply, as well as the social status of its subjects in this country, it early acquired an elite position within the discipline of psychiatry proper. The converse was true of psychiatry as practiced under government auspices, in state, county, and federal mental hospitals. This status differential alone, without reference to the merits of the respective scientific theses, poses a significant barrier to the recruitment of qualified professionals for service in most public institutions. The status difficulty is all the more important when it is compounded by such factors as lower salary, the taxing burden of a heavy patient load, and professional isolation which, in effect, denies the opportunity for future change.

In the face of a change in the role of government as a consequence of the changing structure of Western culture since World War I, it was inevitable that government play an increasingly important role in the problem area of social welfare. From its beginning with compulsory education to the enactment of child labor laws, the establishment and support of public hospitals, the institution of extensive welfare and, now, insurance programs, the expansion of this concern has been a sequence of relatively minor piecemeal adaptations, to use Rostow's phrase, which over-all have brought about a major change in the culture. The creation of the National Institutes of Health provides an example of government's increasing direct and indirect participation in health, education, and welfare areas that previously were the exclusive domains of non-public and individual philanthropic enterprise.

There is much debate over the appropriate balance between private interests and government interests in providing for the welfare of less-advantaged citizens; the medicare program and its insurance benefits for the aged are current cases in point. There are indications, however, that the traditional individualistic values are giving way to what are said to be overriding communal values, a trend sometimes resulting in dissension, confusion, and disharmony that affect other programs. The abridgment of the original community mental health program was clearly a consequence of resistance to this trend.

The post–World War II years have witnessed a shift in social groupings from the individual and small-scale enterprise to the group and large-scale institutions. This shift has led to a bureaucracy which, in turn, has perhaps increasingly encouraged men to express their individuality in areas outside the market place. The increase in the scale and scope of government has shifted a number of loci of power and prestige out of the market place and into service activities of various sorts. Certainly, in recent times the status of the politician and the civil servant has risen immeasurably, and this has apparently extended into the health and welfare fields. The support for medical research and teaching provided by the federal government has made possible a liaison between the university and the government to their mutual advantage. The mutual dependence that derives from this relationship has implications that may serve to breach the status barrier between town and gown, which barrier in the past has been maintained by the fear on each side of being taken over.

Advancing technology has led to the obsolescence in our society of activities, communities, and occupations. Planning, which runs counter to the conventional ethic, has resulted in growth in new directions, but this growth has been idiosyncratic and consequently not all-inclusive. This lack of planning, which is in keeping with the traditional deference to a wholly free and unrestricted enterprise system, has led to a host of traffic jams, both literal and figurative. The high rate of social mobility has contributed to overconcentration in certain areas, and this has had the net effect of restricting mobility in all dimensions. For example, large volumes of material products have been made without regard for demand or usefulness. Automobile production has not been geared to highway building; cities have outgrown their transportation channels. Automation promises to dislocate large blocks of a labor force trained to perform tasks now obsolescent. Conservation of both human and natural resources has had a low priority: maximum use has been made of resources on an *ad hoc* basis with little concern for the long-term consequences. By and large, ingenuity tends to be directed along opportunistic lines with a view to short-term gains.

The value system inherent in frontier psychology leads to a highly competitive territoriality, whose restrictive convenants, secret collusions, need for scapegoats, and consequent discrimination are witnessed in the disadvantaged states of women and of certain races and minority groups. On the other hand, the ecological forces inherent in an exploding population and in accelerated communication require that conflicts be resolved before they reach the flash point; they require integrated, not competitive, service; amalgamation, and not exclusive independence.

The barriers imposed by the changing role of government are therefore many. Although the Jeffersonian notion persists that the primary role of local government is paramount, the transfer of governmental function from local and regional levels to federal levels has been increasing and accelerating. Federal participation in local affairs has been intensified as a result of regulatory commissions and taxation powers as well as the various health, education, and welfare programs that require support beyond the capacity of smaller communities to provide.

As a consequence, the federal government's involvement in health, education, and welfare activities is of significant proportions. This represents, in part, a response to the rise in the public's expectation of the benefits to which it is entitled as a result of the rapid developments in scientific medicine and related disciplines. Coupled with this is an undercurrent of suspicion about the meaning of such reliance, with its threat of control and loss of independence. While the public feels entitled to care, it holds a somewhat unrealistic attitude about costs, which include not only large capital expenditure and a continual outlay for training but also the underwriting of basic and applied research, upon which better care and more service are predicated.

Despite these impediments, government's role in the management of the liberties and welfare of the population has increased substantially, as is evidenced by Defense Department appropriations and the most recently enacted federal legislation in the area of health, education, and welfare. And yet this exercise of positive central authority is a signal which, almost as a rule, alerts opposition.

At our technological society's current state of development, operations are too big and too complex, and the rate of change too dynamic, for it to continue to function under the inherited principles and techniques of non-government. It is as if the issue of power is never squarely faced. Power, in fact, is diffused among many levels of operation, and this very diffusion perpetuates the notion that perhaps, since it is not acknowledged, power does not exist. As various commentators on the current social scene have pointed out, this negative view of power is perhaps the most distinctive aspect of the American point of view. Private power, that is, power exercised at levels of control other than those politically designated, is rationalized to the point where it is not recognized as "power." Only when power bears a governmental imprimatur is it recognized as such, and only then does it seem to generate a quality of opposition which at times, in some quarters, verges on the paranoid.

Obviously, an advancing technological society cannot exist ungoverned (8). There must be a coherent government to orchestrate, regulate, and direct the separate but related activities of groups concerned with matters of great public relevance. Unquestionably, with more and more people living together in the increasingly complicated and interdependent patterns made possible by technology, fewer areas of social life can safely remain ungoverned. Certainly, the areas of health, education, and employment, the organization of living and working areas, and the development of scientific technology require decisive support and control by a governmental authority conscious of and able to use in a positive way its natural powers. One observer has suggested that our adherence to the concept of non-rule is a perfect expression of our unwillingness to abandon the image of infinite individualism.

Quite clearly, in contrast to our myth that we are homogeneous, a society of 196 million persons is characterized by its heterogeneity. The opportunity for truly equal representation of all elements within our society is not available, and the central organization has not been contrived that would provide for carrying out the majority will on every single issue. As a consequence, the unrepresentative quality of the system amounts to disenfranchisement for certain groups at certain times.

One sees reflections of this dilemma within the body of organized medicine. On the one hand, the fact is appreciated that the rising cost of medical care as well as of training and research has to be met by appropriations and subsidies that exceed the capacities of private sources and of local and regional political units, and hence must be assumed in substantial part, directly and indirectly, by the federal government. On the other hand, physicians (at least certain of their organized societies) tend to be distrustful of governmental intent and are suspicious of public health's extension of medical concerns to areas which, in their judgment, are beyond the province of traditional medicine, concerned as it has been with the final expressions of disease.

Dr. Ernest Howard, assistant executive vice-president of the American Medical Association, in November, 1959, at the Sixth Annual Conference of Mental Health Representatives of State Medical Associations, said in discussing "the issues that are confronting the American Medical Association" that "the question of Social Security expansion into the purchase of health benefits" was a "major problem that confronts medicine." He went on to say that that association "is strongly opposed to this legislation for the simple reason that Government intervention of this type, which is purchasing health care for all of these people, is irreversible in nature and will probably gradually extend itself to all of those on the rolls of the Social Security system. This would mean inevitable government control of an unfavorable kind in the practice of medicine."

Among the many derivative problems related to government's role is the issue of interchange between federal and local government and their competition for jurisdiction over programs. The community mental health program will be planned for and administered at the state level. While it is perhaps legally possible to exercise control at the federal level by veto, this would obviously be politically inexpedient. Funds will doubtless have to be made available on the basis of some sort of a population formula, even though such a procedure carries with it the high risk that facilities will be built with greater regard to their pork barrel benefit than to their mental health benefit. The lack of provision for personnel in the present legislation threatens to vitiate the potential benefits of this program. An alternative solution is a mechanism for integrating mental health activities, which can be augmented where needed and when possible. But at the least, a functional, locally supported design is needed which will insure maximum efficiency in the use of existing facilities and services. Certainly, there is no need for another chain of unstaffed marble edifices across the nation, for in effect the present state hospital systems fill such a need.

Public health, along with other areas of concern that lie in the sphere of preventive medicine, has traditionally had a low status in the hierarchy of medical interests (*18*). This seems to be a consequence, in part, of failure to recognize and fully appreciate the fact that the concept of etiology in disease has advanced from a preoccupation with the nature of its physiological expressions to a growing interest in the ecology of all forces, including the socio-environmental ones. For example, while public immunization against infectious disease has become an accepted practice along with the sanitary engineering of water supply and sewage disposal, extension of the same prophylactic principle to the fluoridation of water for control of dental caries and the enactment of social reforms to offset the untoward medical influence of poverty is met by fierce opposition. Manifestly, the proper application of public health measures implies the planning and control of human as well as inanimate factors. Fear of the extension of this planning and control to personal and political spheres is obvious in the contention that they are encroachments upon individual liberty and a step toward socialism.

Psychiatry's position as a specialty practice in relation to medicine has always been an anomalous one. Because its methodologies are for the most part different from those of other medical disciplines, it has had a dubious scientific status. Then, too, in this country its heavy dependence upon Freudian theory has tended to bolster the argument that it is esoteric, metaphysical, and unscientific. Further, the locus of psychiatric practice until recent times has isolated the psychiatrist as well as his patients from the rest of medicine practiced in the community in hospitals and outpatient clinics. Finally, the heavy dependence of the bulk of psychiatric practice on local, state, and federal support and its custodial welfare role have made psychiatry less an "organic" kind of medicine and more a legal-welfare activity, with the invidious overtones that are associated not only with the persons but also with the professions which share this disadvantaged and disenfranchised status.

On a technological level, one of the difficulties in implementing the program of a community mental health center is the traditional compartmentalization of services after the intake procedure. Very few centers have the organization and the cooperative resources necessary to evaluate and to deal adequately with the myriad problems presented by their patient clientele. Consequently, the usual approach is to focus on the diagnostic process and to anchor therapeutic efforts on the one aspect of the patient's problem that the system is equipped to manage. Treatment based on this approach is most often symptomatic and tends to become custodial in one form or another; it rarely extends its horizons beyond the obvious aspects of management. It is this limitation that has coupled with mental illness the requirement of hospitalization and has designated the mentally retarded as more or less irremediable outside of a custodial environment.

The concept of community psychiatry elevates in importance the criterion of the patient's capacity to perform adequately in his social role. It is less concerned with the psychopathological details that can be elicited by a dissecting inquiry, because it recognizes that it is at the level of role-structure that the individual and the social system come into opposition. It is at this level that every man must demonstrate his capacity to meet the expectations of his assigned social roles, and because of this the designation of "illness" or "well-being" is a value judgment rendered on the quality of his social relationships. In this perspective, mental illness is only one of several forms that deviance can take.

A number of studies have documented the nature and appearance of alternative forms of deviance. Starr (26) found that 17 per cent of a sample of thirty-five hundred respondents queried about the gross characteristics of mentally ill persons said that, as they judged it, none of these characteristics was sufficiently deviant to represent what they meant by "mental illness." Another 28 per cent limited their concept of "mental illness" to the "paranoid," for which the distinguishing criterion was violence. Clausen and Yarrow (2) have pointed out that "there is an ethic of being able to handle one's own problem by one's self which applies not only to psychiatric problems." Ewalt (6) has stressed that the outstanding value in American culture compatible with the definition of positive mental health is one that requires that an individual be able to stand on his own two feet without making undo demands or impositions on others.

The feeling is prevalent that psychiatric patients whose major complaints are various somatic symptoms are not abiding by the "rules of the game." According to this reasoning, if these patients were mindful of the "rules," all that would be needed to make them "straighten up and fly right" is to be told that there is nothing physically wrong and that they imagine their difficulties. Such a pejorative attitude constitutes a barrier of discrimination, since it pictures these persons as weak, unfit, less stoical than others, and malingering. In reaction to such an attitudinal set, these persons are loathe to incur disapproval by voluntarily attending a clinic where they will be labeled in terms of the inadequacy, incompetence, and impotence they feel.

A variety of studies (*10, 11, 22*) have shown that lower class status is associated with higher incidence and greater severity of mental disorder, and that persons of this social status are far less likely to receive effective therapy. This raises the question of whether available mental health services can make contact with the deprived residents of the community.

Other studies (*7, 4, 12, 20, 21*) suggest that people in classes equivalent to IV and V in the Hollingshead index are unlikely to be adequately reached by a clinic because they do not tend to use such facilities on a voluntary, self-referred basis for help with problems viewed as psychological.

Walk-in clinics (*20*) have been suggested as a means of overcoming this deficiency. The walk-in clinic at the Metropolitan Hospital in New York City has reported that a six-month sample of such patients indicated that only 20 per cent were gainfully employed, that two-thirds had not graduated from high school, that their median earning was $65 a week (representing a yearly income of $3400), and that only 35.6 per cent were white (40 per cent were born outside of the continental United States). There was an over-all rate of self-referral of 16.4 per cent, representing the less deprived elements of the community. Fifty-five per cent of the group suffered from psychotic reactions, and of the presenting problems, 18.1 per cent were of a social character, 46.7 per cent were psychological, 6.7 per cent physical, and 19.1 per cent both psychological and physical.

The most disorganized families, those providing the least opportunity for meaningful supportive relationships with the community and between parents and siblings, tend to produce patients with the most disorganized and pathological forms of behavior. Thus, the poorly integrated class V families isolated from major community institutions, with overworked, negligent mothers and remote, impulsively brutal fathers, tend to produce schizophrenic patients. The world of the class V is characterized by pervasive and unpredictable aggression (19).

Srole and Langner (25) point out that the status system is an apparatus that differentially sows, reaps, sifts, and redistributes the community's crops of mental morbidity and of sound personalities. They implicate certain specific forms of socio-cultural processes that operate within the framework of the social class system, and they suggest that economic factors are involved in the mechanisms of invidious discrimination that pervades the various ways of life of these persons. Toward one end of the status range, in both preadult and adult life, these processes tend to penetrate the family unit with eugenic or prophylactic effects for personality development, whereas toward the opposite pole they more often work with pathogenic or precipitating effects. Specifically at or near the poverty level, Srole and Langner discern particularly heavy pathogenic weights currently bearing on the especially vulnerable people. Those handicapped in personality or lacking in social assets from childhood on are trapped as adults at or near the poverty level, there to find themselves enmeshed in the web of burdens that tends to precipitate or intensify mental and somatic morbidity. This precipitation in turn accelerates descent into the chronic, personality-crushing indigency which Srole and Langner suggest is America's own displaced person's problem. They also conclude, in comprehensive terms, that there are many more mentally impaired people among the poor than among the affluent; that poor people far more often get less psychiatric attention; and that when they do get attention, the outcome less often appears to be a significant and sustained gain.

In a single month in 1962, almost one and a quarter million persons received $77 billion in monthly disability benefits under the disability insurance program of the Social Security Administration. Fourth in prevalence among disabling conditions were mental disorders, which accounted for 10 per cent of all claims allowed. A study of two thousand psychiatric consultations purchased during 1961 by state agencies revealed that the cost of the consultations was nearly $1 million (27).

Lawrence (17) shows that the prevalence of chronic diseases increased progressively from among the well-to-do to among the very poor between the years 1923 and 1943. Then, too, chronic diseases are of greater significance than any other factor in leading to a lowered economic status and a loss of social position.

These investigations are indicative of an emerging and expanding conception of epidemiology. Overcrowded dwelling units have long been known to be an important factor in the spread of communicable disease; similarly, in a rapidly changing society, anxiety-inducing elements are carried along in the traditions of the society and outlive the capacity of medicine to free the individual from their consequences. At present, the dyadic patient-physician relationship as an unaffiliated social institution is faced with but is often unable to assume responsibilities that formerly, in a small, well-knit culture, were spread over many institutions. Hence, the need exists for another treatment modality within the community organized on a different basis.

The extent to which qualities ideally defined as essential to the therapeutic relationship will be present in a given professional relationship varies inversely with the degree of social distance. There is evidence of reluctance on the part of class IV and V patients to participate in the kind of interchange necessary for adequate administration of psycho-social therapeutic remedies.

Public health has, inevitably, incorporated society's dominant middle-class values, those stemming from the Protestant ethic which assumes them to be universally meaningful and desirable. However, class differences may substantially limit the degree of congruence possible between these precepts and the felt-needs of the lower-class public.

For middle-class people, cleanliness, which at times can approach compulsive proportions, is an index to the morals and virtue of the individual, and these people place great emphasis on the ability to defer gratifications in the interest of long-term goals. The middle class also accords high value to rationality, and its ethos condones foresight, deliberate planning, and efficient allocation of resources.

This emphasis on future-time orientation may not be particularly meaningful to lower-status people and consequently may constitute a considerable barrier to well intentioned psychotherapeutic efforts (16). The norms also prescribe a strong sense of individual responsibility, which places a premium on resourcefulness and self-reliance. These ideals are frequently built into public goals, so that the object of health education undertaken by community clinics becomes the inculcation in each individual of a sense of responsibility for his own health. Middle-class socialization patterns tend to be consistently organized in accordance with emphasis on effort and achievement, and, as a result, children of this class are subject to a considerable amount of supervision and control.

Jahoda (13) has pointed out that the efforts of social scientists in the area of mental disease are a recent innovation; that up to now this area has been a medical domain; and that the newcomer has not everywhere been received with open arms. The idea that social scientists can contribute to the understanding of mental health problems is still regarded with suspicion in some quarters.

The Joint Commission's study, *Community Resources in Mental Health* (23), points out that for decades public health leaders have included mental health or mental hygiene among their central interests. However, there is considerable disparity between the level of general health services and that of public health representatives' participation or interest in mental health services. This disparity is due to the fact that in some communities, leadership in mental health is taken by other official or voluntary bodies. In other settings, programs in other fields absorb the public health staff's time and energy.

The public health nurse, for example, despite the locus of her employment, is increasingly called upon to exert her influence in the social and emotional problems of her patients. Public health nurses seem to be natural agents for carrying out in practice with patients and their families any new or enlarged program involving face-to-face relationships with people.

The complex social and economic characteristics that vary from community to community and the great variety of configurations of community resources constitute another problem. Few communities have, in all the relevant areas, specialists available to master the intricacies and the ramifications of these problems. Those that do would often benefit from the help of outsiders, whose neutrality and experience with similar issues would permit a clearer view of the obstructions at hand.

Up to now, experience in supplying consultation service suggests the importance of a generic approach to the problem of planning for coordination of mental health resources. The cooperation of outside consultants and locally recruited staff in solving a specific problem, such as organizing clinical services, is not enough. An adequate community mental health program demands a far more comprehensive arrangement. Consultative groups must meet with and advise representative community groups on their role in planning the allocation and development of a whole range of resources. Anything short of this constitutes an insurmountable barrier to the accomplishment of a truly comprehensive program.

Walter Boek (1) outlines a model for community action that is intended to circumvent organizational barriers. He proposes a behind-the-scenes attack on the decision-making power structure in the following six steps: (1) informing the executive committee of the Board of Health; (2) conferring with leaders of the power structure; (3) involving community professionals; (4) stimulating citizen interest; (5) securing support from leaders; and (6) obtaining action from policymakers.

Willie and Notkin (28), dealing specifically with the problem of the city of Syracuse, have reported on the function of the community seminar, and the conclusions of their study correspond to the findings of a national study of 218 communities. Using hospital construction as a prototypal instance, it was found that a long and gradual period of development, lasting from two to ten years, occurs between the first interest in constructing a hospital and the initial action on the project.

Such an enterprise is primarily a masculine one: two-thirds of the active participants are either businessmen, professional men, managers, or executives. Very seldom were the projects initiated by single individuals. Campaigns were usually launched by voluntary associations organized for that specific purpose, and existing community groups were seldom asked to assume the responsibility for implementing such a comprehensive project. The proper and appropriate representation of the sponsoring group on the governing board is always a difficult problem in the early stages of community organization, and most communities recommended the careful use of surveys and outside consultants in implementing the project. Most groups had the persistent problem of justifying the need to the community.

When professionals are committed to behavior which is delayed in its consummation, the possibility of negative consequences creates a situation ripe with what Festinger has called dissonance. The inconsistency between competitive motives and the knowledge that it will be some time before motivation is reduced necessitate the reduction of dissonance. This ordinarily is accomplished by a reduction in the intensity of the consummatory and instrumental behavior involved.

This partially explains referral drop-out, the "loss" of patients in the transfer between services. Unless the response to a referral request is reinforced by a positive feedback in accordance with professional expectations, the less involved service tends to withdraw its interest and attention.

In order to achieve a closer cognitive interaction among physicians, their professional roles must be planned so as to be congruent. A workable interchange of efforts depends upon the structured congeniality of the organization.

A deficiency in any of these areas—community planning, professional involvement, utilization of the existing power structure—creates a barrier to any attempt to reconcile overlapping and competing bureaucracies (9). The federal-state relationship has been cited as a political institutional example of the same phenomenon of multiple and interdependent control.

The legislation that implements the community mental health program provides funds for physical facilities but not the means to secure a staff. An immediate consequence of this legislative compromise has been a downgrading of the program. Without the control that staffing would provide there is a likelihood that local planning groups will formulate programs of many different kinds and purposes. It seems reasonable to anticipate that efforts will be made to locate the new physical facilities primarily in areas of the states where they will benefit the local economy. If the many questions posed by the multiple objectives of the program are to be answered, replicated research is necessary. A prerequisite for this is a series of model programs in different regions. Only through these can the experiential data be gathered that are necessary for adequate quality control. Without co-ordination, staffing, involvement, and the other programmatic essentials, the barriers to the acquisition of these data are formidable, and extensions of these barriers to operations at the federal level are foreseeable. There is a division of authority and responsibility among the administrative groups concerned with the building of hospitals, those concerned with the creation of the programs to be housed in them, and the specialists, the architects and engineers, who are concerned with cost and technical details. The potential for dissonance among these groups is high, and since coordinated planning is essential, it could impede the development of the program on a national scale.

Another barrier arises at the operational level when a choice must be made between alternative policies. Some view the comprehensive mental health program as an opportunity for a radical departure from traditional medical and psychiatric preoc-cupations. They look toward a clearer definition of the ecological forces behind mental health problems, for example, poverty, educational disadvantage, and the community and family ante-cedents of dislocation. The group that determines policy at local, regional, and national levels will naturally commit the program to predefined ends. For instance, there is an understandable profes-sional interest on the part of psychiatrists in emphasizing the clinical psychiatric therapeutic resources of mental health cen-ters. One objection to this is economic. The cost of establishing a psychiatric treatment facility for every 100,000 persons in the country is of such magnitude that if it were done, there would be little likelihood of being able to afford anything else. An opposing view is that the program should pursue non-therapeutic objectives, such as collation of much-needed social data, which is said to be necessary if one is to do more than manage the effects of mental illness.

There are other barriers as well. If a center is to function as an evaluation clearinghouse, there must be no bars to eligibility for a diagnostic evaluation. Current politico-medical philosophy precludes the establishment of an open service. Any plan for diagnostic evaluation that does not limit its service to the medically indigent is construed as the entering wedge into an era of socialized medicine. Thus the crucial technical problem of identifying those para-psychiatric cases whose problems manifest themselves in a symptomatic form beyond the traditional province of medicine becomes the more difficult.

All of this is concerned with the traffic control operations of the center. Most centers have found that, if accurate registry data are to be collected, intake must be limited to an arbitrarily defined population area. This means, of course, that those outside the designated area are automatically denied the services of the center. Adherence to this policy could lead to strained intergroup relations. On the other hand, with the limited amount of money available for carrying out multiple functions, an open-end policy would mean that the centers would quickly be overwhelmed, and that demands for service would preclude the support of research.

The following outline describes fifteen areas that are most likely to become barriers to the creation of an effective comprehensive community mental health center:

1. Unless the right combination of power influences within the community can be mustered at the right time, there is likely to be resistance to the acceptance of a mental health center that calls itself "comprehensive." The new facility is likely to be viewed as another competitor in the hierarchy of existing community services.

2. There are, at present and for the foreseeable future, staggering shortages in all categories of personnel. This deficiency will become worse because of the failure to provide sufficient funds for personnel.

3. The size of the nationwide mental health problem, even

within its narrowest institutional definitions, precludes the development of anything more than a small pilot community program in a few representative centers.

A Joint Commission study of the ratio of manpower to population in fifteen counties indicates wide variance in the ratios for psychologists and graduate social workers. The best supplied county had one psychiatrist per 25,000 population, the worst one per 148,000. Similarly, for psychologists, the best supplied county had one per 14,000, the worst one per 73,000. For social workers, the best had one per 5,000, the worst one per 95,000.

4. The mental health problem has many guises, not the least of which is the mask of physical disability which hides personal, family, community, and cultural disorganization. If the term "comprehensive" is to have operational meaning, new methods for case-finding will have to be devised.

5. There are inter- and intra-organizational problems, a significant number of which derive from the mixed character of mental health problems. These require detailed elaboration by a trained multidisciplinary staff in order to achieve a clear definition of operational direction before the inauguration of services.

6. Since current legislation does not restrict the benefits of this program to certain categories of citizens, local planning groups will of necessity be confronted with the problem of financial eligibility. This is likely to mean the establishment of a variety of means tests. Such a step runs counter to the basis of a general evaluation procedure—the assumption that every problem that presents itself is remediable.

7. This opens the question of referral barriers. Mental health problems, to a considerable degree, lie in a gray area. It is the prevailing social climate which determines what properly is remediable (and hence eligible) and what is not.

8. Since the comprehensive community mental health center is a new facility and is likely to be viewed as a competitor, it runs two risks: that of being unacceptable as a member of the medical organizational elite; and that of becoming a dumping ground for the unsolved problems that currently tax existing medical facilities and welfare agencies.

9. Related to this are the difficulties to be encountered in interagency cooperation.

10. The problem of autonomy among federated agencies involved in a new joint activity is a thorny one. While it is generally agreed that it is desirable for a center to represent the pooled mental health interests of the community, the problem of changing the current arrangement of power influences to permit this is unsolved.

11. There are a host of legal and professional barriers to the creation of a common record, which is a prerequisite for any meaningful research into the incidence and prevalence of mental health problems.

12. The number, complexion, and variety of the personnel who must collaborate in a center will raise the issue of administrative control, which has for some time plagued the mental health field.

13. There are difficulties to be confronted in establishing the range of functions that are essential if the center is to operate on a comprehensive level. Its outpatient facilities will of necessity be limited. The number of child psychiatrists, for example, is very limited, but their participation is vital to many functions of a truly comprehensive center, such as collaboration with school authorities and with the local courts and welfare agencies. The demand and the supply are irreconcilable.

14. It is conceivable that the demands for service and consultation merely from community agencies and hospitals, who will except reciprocal cooperation from a mental health center, once it is accepted, will be overwhelming.

15. Inasmuch as legislative action has separated programmatic from architectural planning, it is very likely that the final architectural plans will, in many instances, be at considerable variance with the needs of the program that will ultimately use the center.

References

1 BOEK, W. E. Social science applied to the dynamics of community process. *Adult Education* 7:174–78, 192, 1957.

2 CLAUSEN, J. A., AND YARROW, M. R. Paths to the mental hospital. *J. soc. Issues* 11:25–32, 1955.

3 COLEMAN, J. V. A community project for the cooperative care of mental hospital patients: The cooperative care project. *Amer. J. Psychiat.* 119:729–31, 1963.

4 COLEMAN, J., *et al.* A comparative study of a psychiatric clinic and a family agency. Part I. *Soc. Casewk. 38:*3, 1957. Part II. *Soc. Casewk. 38:*74, 1957.

5 CUMMING, E., AND CUMMING, J. *Closed Ranks.* Cambridge, Harvard Univ. Press, 1957.

6 EWALT, J. E. In *Current Concepts of Positive Mental Health,* edited by M. Jahoda. New York, Basic Books, 1958, p. xi.

7 FREEDMAN, L. A., AND HOLLINGSHEAD, A. B. *Amer. J. Psychiat. 113:*769, 1957.

8 GOERKE, L. S. Health and urban development. III. The relationship of health agencies and planning agencies. *Amer. J. Public Health 54:*713–20, 1964.

9 GOSS, M. E. W. Influence and authority among physicians in an outpatient clinic. *Amer. sociol. Rev. 26:*39–50, 1961.

10 HOLLINGSHEAD, A. B., AND REDLICH, F. C. *Social Class and Mental Illness.* New York, Wiley, 1958.

11 HUNT, R. G. Socio-cultural factors in mental disorder. *Behav. Sci. 4:*96, 1959.

12 IMBER, S. D., *et al.* Suggestibility, social class, and the acceptance of psychotherapy. *J. clin. Psychol. 12:*341, 1956.

13 JAHODA, M. Environment and mental health. *Int. soc. Sci. J. 11:*14, 1959.

14 JOINT COMMISSION ON MENTAL ILLNESS AND HEALTH. *Action for Mental Health.* New York, Basic Books, 1961.

15 KATZ, E., LEVIN, M. L., AND HAMILTON, H. Traditions of research on the diffusion of innovation. *Amer. sociol. Rev. 28:*237–52, 1963.

16 KLEINER, R. J., AND PARKER, S. Goal-striving, social status and mental disorder. A research review. *Amer. sociol. Rev. 28:*189–203, 1963.

17 LAWRENCE, P. S. Chronic illness and social economic status. *Public Health Reports. 63:*1507–21, 1948.

18 LEFCOWITZ, M. J. The public health professional: A marginal man. *Amer. J. Public Health 54:*1125–28, 1964.

19 MYERS, J. K., AND ROBERTS, B. H. *Family and Class Dynamics in Mental Illness.* New York, Wiley, 1959.

20 NORMAN, W., FENSTERHEIM, H., TANNENBAUM, G., AND SAGER, C. J. The acceptance of the psychiatric walk-in clinic in a highly deprived community. *Amer. J. Psychiat. 120:*533–39, 1963.

21 REDLICH, F. C., *et al.* Social class differences in attitudes toward psychiatry. *Amer. J. Orthopsychiat. 25:*60, 1955.

22 RENNIE, T. A. C., *et al.* Urban life and mental health. *Amer. J. Psychiat. 113:*831, 1957.

23 ROBINSON, R., DeMARCHE, D. F., AND WAGLE, M. D. *Community Resources in Mental Health.* New York, Basic Books, 1960, p. 17.

24 SCHWARTZ, M. S., AND SCHWARTZ, C. G. *Social Approaches to Mental Patient Care.* New York, Columbia Univ. Press, 1964.

25 SROLE, L., AND LANGNER, T. S. "Socio-economic Status Groups: Their
    Mental Health Composition." In *Mental Health in the Metropolis*, by
    L. Srole, T. S. Langner, S. T. Michael, M. D. Opler, and T. A. D.
    Rennie. New York, McGraw-Hill, 1962.
26 STAR, S. In D. L. Phillips, Rejection: A possible consequence of
    seeking help for mental disorders. *Amer. sociol. Rev.* 28:963–72, 1963.
27 U.S. DEPT. OF COMMERCE. *Statistical Abstract of the United States.*
    83rd annual edition. U.S. Gov't. Printing Office, 1962.
28 WILLIE, C. V., AND NOTKIN, H. "Community Organization for Health:
    A Case Study." In *Patients, Physicians and Illness: Source Book in
    Behavioral Science and Medicine,* edited by E. G. Jaco. Glencoe,
    Illinois, Free Press, 1958, p. 149.

Three

Community Psychiatry
Some Troubling Questions

SEYMOUR L. HALLECK, M.D.

PSYCHIATRY's failure to provide high standards of care for a major portion of the mentally ill is being critically examined and new models, which, it is hoped, will meet these needs through a community-oriented approach, are being proposed. Community psychiatry holds many hopes for the conscientious professional. It promises to draw psychiatry closer to general medicine and public service by bringing it out of the cloistered aura of the analytic consultation room and away from the remote wards of the mental hospital. It holds out the possibility of developing preventive measures which might decrease the incidence of mental illness. Most important, it suggests the means by which the benefits of psychiatric knowledge can be brought to the poor as well as to the hundreds of thousands of socially disorganized individuals who up to now have been deprived of the best psychiatric care.

The concept of community psychiatry is so broad in scope that its potential repercussions upon our profession and our society are extremely difficult to predict. Certainly, psychiatric practice may well change more radically in the next ten years than in any decade our profession has known. If these changes are to provide

57

maximum benefit, it is essential that psychiatrists make some effort to anticipate their direction and consequences. The benefits that we hope to gain through community psychiatry are many and have been well documented here and elsewhere (3, 1). It may be equally important, however, to make a serious effort to anticipate the possible undesirable consequences of this new movement. My efforts in this paper will be to examine critically certain directions in community psychiatry which could produce new problems for us and for our patients. Questions will be raised which may at first glance appear to be tangential or insignificant. If any of these issues, however, stimulate us to actions that may prevent even the smallest of undesirable consequences, they will be worth our thoughtful attention.

Before attempting to examine the possible undesirable consequences of community psychiatry, it is necessary to define clearly the potentially troubling directions of this movement. Community psychiatry encompasses so many different kinds of activities that it would be grossly unfair to raise critical issues without explicitly noting that they are relevant only to certain limited directions of the movement.

Community psychiatry is most frequently described as encompassing five major activities or functions:

1. Attempts to counteract the debilitating effects of institutionalization by improving mental hospitals and by making sustained efforts to treat as many serious cases as possible outside of the hospital—that is, in the community. Development of open-door hospitals, therapeutic communities within hospitals, day hospitals, and aftercare programs is an example of effort in this direction.

2. Efforts to educate the public, particularly those involved in caretaker professions, to understand the psychiatric basis of deviant behavior and particularly to understand the dynamics of interpersonal relationships. Lectures, discussion groups, and even programed courses in interpersonal relations have been employed as instruments in this endeavor.

3. A commitment to consult with community agencies dealing with social disorganization (agencies concerned, for example, with alcoholism, the aged, education of retarded children, or

crime). This commitment may be restricted to purely educative activities, in which case it is similar to the second function. But it also includes efforts to supervise, direct, and, on occasion, interpret the work of the agency employee, or to advise and treat clients for which the agency is responsible.

4. Efforts to provide total psychiatric care to a carefully defined and limited social unit such as a neighborhood, a county, an industrial corporation, or a university. The commitment here is to deal with all of the mental health problems in that unit. It is not restricted to offering help only to those who ask for it. This approach includes case-finding techniques designed to treat those who trouble the community, and the psychiatrist attempts to utilize all community resources in his rehabilitative efforts. This approach also emphasizes the importance of brief therapies and early medical intervention in crisis situations.

5. Involvement in the major administrative decisions of our society. Some psychiatrists believe that the community psychiatrist must become involved in this area. According to Caplan (2), one purpose of community psychiatry is "to provide services to assist people facing stress, to healthier problem solving by means of governmental or other administrative action. The object is to influence law, statutes, regulations and customs in order to achieve these ends."

The activities described under 1 and 2, and to a certain extent under 3, are certainly not new. They reflect the impact of enlightened attitudes and greater knowledge on our treatment of the mentally ill. The dangers of prolonged hospitalization have become increasingly apparent. It makes sense to treat the disturbed individual in as close proximity to the source of his difficulties as is possible—that is, within the community. Similarly, increased sharing of our knowledge with the public is long overdue. The activities involved in functions 1 and 2, and to some extent 3, represent an evolution toward greater community-mindedness and a recognition of the importance of social factors in the problems of mental illness. It is extremely unlikely that acceleration of such activities could have any undesirable consequences.

On the other hand, the activities involved in part of function 3 and all of functions 4 and 5 seem to be new and different. Involvement in these activities constitutes enough of a change in philosophy and practice that some have talked of a "third psychiatric revolution." All of the doubts and questions that will be developed in the following discussion relate to the last three functions. Although the generic term "community psychiatry" will be used for the sake of convenience, it should be understood that any critical references made in this paper are applicable only to these particular community-oriented activities.

If implementation of community approaches to mental health problems leads to the creation of new and perhaps greater problems, our profession will be faced with certain dilemmas. Some of the potential problems have been recognized; others have not. An unexamined and unplanned growth of community psychiatry could have at least five major undesirable results:

1. Community psychiatry could require alteration of the traditional values that have served the medical profession for over two thousand years.

2. Community psychiatry could be abused in a manner that would lead to undesirable limitations of our traditional freedoms.

3. Community psychiatry could involve the physician in political decision-making that is beyond his qualifications or interests.

4. Community psychiatry could lead to an emphasis on medical administrative skills at the expense of services that physicians alone can offer.

5. Community psychiatry, in its efforts to serve all of the citizens of the community, could paradoxically encourage the perpetuation of differential treatment according to class.

COMMUNITY PSYCHIATRY AND TRADITIONAL VALUES

Community psychiatry seems to encourage our profession to deal with varieties of behavior that are not entirely familiar to the psychiatrist. Until recently, psychiatry's involvement in problems such as delinquency, school adjustment, aging, and alcoholism has for the most part been confined to the examination and treatment of individual cases. When the psychiatrist examines the problem of deviant behavior, he enters a complicated borderline area. Many forms of social maladjustment have traditionally been considered in the legal or cultural province rather than the medical. It is true that, when we come to know the socially maladjusted individual, we often discover that he is a chronically unhappy person who experiences emotional conflicts and problems of adaptation almost identical to those we see in people whom we define as mentally ill. Unless the physician examines each case individually, however, the application of principles of mental hygiene to problems of social deviancy becomes extraordinarily complicated and obscure.

Without a painstaking and critical examination of this extremely complicated problem, the possibility that community involvement will lead to unplanned and unnoticed shifts in our professional commitments is increased. It is not impossible that adjustment to the needs of others could become our most important goal in the treatment of disturbed people. The psychiatrist who consults to welfare agencies may be asked to help the agency worker in the latter's efforts to encourage clients to accept difficult social situations. The psychiatrist who commits himself to the health needs of the total community may find himself relying on briefer therapies, which do not increase the strength of the personality and which may emphasize effective coping rather than alleviation of suffering. Once committed to such activities, the physician tends to become more involved in the needs of the community and somewhat less dedicated to the wishes and needs of his patient. He could eventually abandon his role as the patient's agent.

Certain activities of community psychiatry imply a subtle but important shift in value orientation. While it is often true that the person who adjusts to the needs of others is also a comfortable person, there are many exceptions to this statement. Adjustment through conformity or even through more active attempts to cope with a situation is not always compatible with the individual's wishes or needs. Maintenance of an adequate level of performance may serve the needs of others but may be quite expensive to the individual. Traditionally, medical values have put primary emphasis on the patient's comfort.

There are obviously no simple right or wrong answers to this problem. In many instances a good case can be made for holding

the values of adjustment and coping above the values of alleviation of individual suffering. This is ordinarily true in wartime or
when a patient's behavior represents a serious threat to the
welfare of the community. The military physician is required to
hold the values of conformity and coping above many others.
Every physician has at times found himself bound by conditions
which require that he consider the needs of the community above
those of the patient. Generally, however, we tend to avoid such
situations, and primarily we value our ability to serve the patient.

If community psychiatry leads us to deal with the broader
aspects of social maladjustment, new dimensions of medical
responsibility will be created. We will move into strange and
uncharted territories. The physician has few ground rules or
ethical standards available to him when he is forced to choose in
favor of either the individual or the community. One of psychiatry's most important needs in the future may be for new
codes that will guide the conduct of the physician who wishes to
contribute to the alleviation of social distress.

COMMUNITY PSYCHIATRY AND TRADITIONAL FREEDOMS

Recently certain groups in our country have been impressed
with the dangers of giving psychiatry too much power to control
deviant behavior. The psychiatrist, according to some of our
critics (6, 5), is a person who could use his medical power to socially immobilize those who hold deviant political or ethical beliefs.* Our critics tend to exaggerate unduly the possible dangers
and seem at times to be insensitive to the positive humanistic
gains derived through applying the medical model to certain
forms of maladaptive behavior. Nevertheless, there is a certain
amount of poignancy in their warnings. Their concerns are especially relevant when applied to some of the possible misuses of
community psychiatry.

It seems likely that the growth of community psychiatry will
encourage society to consider certain deviant behaviors as forms

---

* It seems to me that these writers miss the point in seeing the psychiatrist as
the active instigator of questionable social interference. It is much more likely that
the psychiatrist is himself in danger of being used by various segments of society
to further goals he himself would eschew.

of mental illness. Behaviors defined as mental illness are more likely to encourage public action than those defined as peculiarity, rebelliousness, or social disorganization. For the most part, public arousal is desirable where human suffering is concerned. We cannot, however, ignore certain undesirable social consequences which occur when deviant behaviors formerly defined in social or legal terms are re-defined as mental illness.

This problem is best clarified by a hypothetical example. A psychiatrist is asked to help the community (through either an agency consultation, assistance with legislation, or his administrative function) in dealing with three men who have been arrested for committing acts of civil disobedience. The first claims that he is protesting the fact that Negroes are now being given too many privileges. The second claims that he is protesting nuclear armament. The third is a southern Negro who is attempting to protest the fact that he has been deprived of his right to vote. Any one of these men could have been motivated by pathological conflict or irrational thinking. Yet each of them is expressing a distinct (and, to his mind, a defensible) social viewpoint. The psychiatrist, after thoroughly examining them, might conclude that none should be considered mentally ill. No matter what he concludes, however, his decision has crucial implications. If any one of these men were labeled ill, his social protest would be nullified or rendered ineffective. The social pronouncements of a person considered mentally ill are not usually taken seriously.

Herein lies the danger of psychiatrists and psychiatry being misused in a way that threatens the right of individual dissent. There are an infinite number of behaviors which, although strange or even unlawful, serve a definite social purpose. If a community considered such behaviors to be noxious and employed a psychiatrist to assist in invalidating their social meaning, some of our traditional freedoms would be in danger.

Most psychiatrists are far more aware of these dangers than our critics give us credit for. But, on the other hand, we derive much protection from a commitment to an individually oriented approach in which diagnosis is arrived at only after painstaking and careful examination of each case. Do those community approaches that emphasize brief therapy, consultation, and social planning give the individual the same protection? Do they allow the physician to plan carefully for the best possible treatment or social disposition of each individual patient? These are neither insignificant nor farfetched questions. Anyone who doubts the potential abuses of psychiatry need only examine precedents in the Soviet Union to discover the grotesque injustices that can be perpetrated under the guise of medical treatment. And if we feel that "it can't happen here," we cannot be reassured by the fact that a reputable magazine during the recent presidential campaign polled thirteen thousand psychiatrists and asked them to answer yes or no to the question of the psychological fitness of a major presidential candidate. To our credit, the majority of psychiatrists refused to participate in this "poll." The possibility that psychiatrists would consider answering this question either affirmatively or negatively without ever having examined the individual in question is, however, troubling.

We live in a world that is changing at a truly incredible rate. Overpopulation, automation, and a shift from rural to urban patterns of life have brought new social problems that stagger the imagination. The psychiatric profession is only one of many that has been urgently called upon to help society maintain its mastery of forces largely created by man himself. The issues that have been raised here relate to psychiatry and the rights of the individual, particularly his rights to privacy and freedom. We must acknowledge the possibility that such individual rights may, of necessity, have to undergo modification or abridgment in a mass society. This, too, is an area which warrants our profession's careful attention and study.

COMMUNITY PSYCHIATRY AND PHYSICIANS' POLITICAL DECISION-MAKING

Once the psychiatrist involves himself in the problems of the community, he finds that it is almost impossible to avoid an imposition of his own political values or viewpoints upon the society. Let us suppose that he is determined to avoid social commentary and that he agrees only to be available to treat any aspect of social disorganization that the community refers to him. He then finds himself treating certain disturbances that can also be considered by-products of poverty or of cultural conflict. In doing this, he may be giving the community an opportunity to rationalize or ignore the social conditions that have created the disturbance in the first place. If a psychiatrist is available to treat the casualties of social conflict, the need to change the conditions that produced the disorder is diminished.

I recognize, of course, that most psychiatrists would not content themselves with a casualty-oriented approach. This possibility is advanced only to illustrate the fact that any action we take in dealing with a community problem involves a social and political judgment as to the kind of community we hope to live in. Neutrality is not possible. A casualty-oriented approach can be misconstrued as a vote of confidence for the status quo. An approach directed toward active social change would inevitably reflect a psychiatric position as to the type of political values the community should adopt.

What is right or wrong for our profession in this situation is a complex and bewildering question. The only thing that is clear is that increasing involvement in community psychiatry compels us to take more forceful stands on political issues. This is not necessarily bad. Physicians have at various times become deeply involved in political struggles. Other professional groups such as atomic scientists have seen such activities as a moral responsibility. But there does appear to be an urgent need to recognize the existence of these problems and to clarify our own stands. Psychiatrists are a diversified group whose members hold to differing political and ethical commitments. We will need guidelines, in this case, to help us differentiate between those instances in which we speak as medical scientists and those in which we speak as advocates of a social viewpoint.

The complexities of this problem seem endless. In our efforts to predict the consequences of a community approach to psychiatry, we must recognize that not only does the psychiatrist have the power to influence the social and political climate of his community, but he himself is deeply influenced by that same climate. To a large extent, the modes of psychiatric practice are determined by the values of the community. Community psychiatry has made its greatest strides in nations deeply committed to public welfare programs. The impetus of the growth of this movement in our own country is not unrelated to the emergence of welfare-oriented political philosophies. If government is to support the kind of benevolent community psychiatry we are experiencing in our nation today, it must be strongly determined to help its underprivileged, its misfits, and its deviants. A "community psychiatry" in Nazi Germany might have been quite a different story, and a community psychiatry in a nation of "rugged individualists" would be an impossibility.

COMMUNITY PSYCHIATRY IN RELATION TO DEPLOYMENT OF MEDICAL RESOURCES

A major implication of community psychiatry is that the physician must devote himself to a greater number of administrative roles. It is appropriate to ask if such roles are best fitted to the talents of the physician. How many of us should become experienced in dealing with such problems as mobilization of community resources or the development of programs for long-range community planning? There have always been a certain number of psychiatrists endowed with special skills and motivations who have devoted their careers to administrative and preventive psychiatry. The rapid growth of community psychiatry, however, suggests that far more than a small proportion of psychiatrists will be called upon to elect this subspecialty as a career. Will this require specialized training beyond that ordinarily provided in a three-year residency program? In an already overburdened profession, this could represent a new demand for expenditure of manpower and time.

Are other professionals such as psychologists, social workers, or sociologists equally capable of administrating community health activities? Certainly medical responsibilities have to be retained by the psychiatrist. But there is ample evidence that non-psychiatric administrators can do competent jobs in such activities as case-finding, facilitating the communication process, education, social planning, and day-to-day administration. Does community psychiatry call for a commitment of the physician's services to the performance of functions that could in fact be fulfilled by others? Some psychiatrists will always be needed in administrative roles, but the psychiatric profession and the public might lose a great deal if a major portion of our younger colleagues chose to devote more time to administration and less to clinical practice. The psychiatrist would move closer to the public, but his greater visibility would not be in those roles that he performs best.

COMMUNITY PSYCHIATRY AND PSYCHIATRIC CARE FOR THE POOR

The most exciting aspect of the community-oriented approach to psychiatry is the hope that it holds out for better psychiatric treatment for the poor. Present psychiatric facilities for treatment of the underprivileged are grievously limited. Even where low-cost psychiatric services are provided, there is a disturbing tendency to offer lower class people forms of treatment that symbolize less status (4). Most psychiatrists are shamed and troubled by these discrepancies, which are not paralleled in any other specialty of medical practice.

The proposed directions of community psychiatry, however, present limited solutions to this problem and may be neglecting some of the more promising possibilities. They may, in fact, almost paradoxically serve to strengthen current inequalities. Although this movement could bring many new services to the lower classes, it is unlikely that it will emphasize intensive psychotherapy. Rather, devices such as brief psychotherapy, counseling, drug therapy, and environmental manipulation will be utilized. It is also likely that even if a comprehensive community program is fully implemented, members of the upper classes will (as they have thus far in Great Britain) continue to seek long-term psychotherapy for their personal problems. Thus, although community psychiatry attempts to diminish some of the inequalities in the levels of treatment available to different classes, it does not begin to approach final solutions.

Is there an alternative approach that would provide adequate levels of psychiatric care for all classes of people? Are there ways of bringing the benefits of our techniques of psychotherapy to larger groups? At first glance this appears to be an overwhelming task. Our profession has not fully examined this question, how-ever, and the possibilities are not totally exhausted. Would a concerted effort to train even greater numbers of individual psychotherapists, group therapists, or family therapists represent a wiser investment of our nation's resources than the current directions of the new community programs? This is a debatable issue on which there has, unfortunately, been insufficient debate.

SUMMARY AND CONCLUSIONS

My purpose has been to remind the reader of some possible consequences, unplanned and unanticipated, of a new dimension of psychiatric practice. Not everyone would see all of these as undesirable. What is important is that the profession recognize the possibility that they will occur. If efforts are made to predict the potential epiphenomena of community psychiatry, their subsequent evaluation in terms of desirability will be facilitated.

Those who, at present, detect undesirable qualities in these potential developments are concerned with the following questions:

1. What happens when the physician involves himself in the coping and adjustment problems of individuals who, up to now, have not been defined as patients? Are modifications needed in the ethical codes of our profession?

2. Is there a possibility that the community could utilize psychiatric resources in ways that might limit individual rights? If this could happen, should we try to prevent it? How can we devise standards that will help us to balance the needs of the community against the rights of the individual?

3. Are psychiatrists sufficiently aware of the political and moral implications of their community work? Can we devise codes or ground rules that will allow us to speak out sensibly on those political and moral issues that do seem to be related to mental health, without overstepping the bounds of scientific rigor or becoming insensitive proponents of a political viewpoint?

4. Does community psychiatry encourage the young psychiatrist to neglect his investment in traditional clinical activities? Could some of the administrative roles he will be asked to assume be capably filled by other professionals?

5. Is it likely that community psychiatry will provide equal treatment for the poor? Are there other means by which adequate

levels of psychiatric treatment for all classes of people could be assured?

In presenting this troubled viewpoint, I do not intend to discourage or deprecate efforts that have had a revitalizing effect upon our profession. The community psychiatry movement has encouraged us to deal with problems which previously, with feelings of ineffectiveness and guilt, were suppressed. However, any new movement that attempts to resolve long-standing problems must, inevitably, raise problems of its own. Faced with our nation's overwhelming mental health needs, the psychiatric physician, more than ever before, will have need of a painstaking examination of the impact of his new techniques upon his profession and his patients.

References

1 BELLAK, LEOPOLD, ED. *Handbook of Community Psychiatry and Community Mental Health.* New York, Grune & Stratton, 1964.
2 CAPLAN, GERALD. *An Approach to Community Mental Health.* New York, Grune & Stratton, 1961.
3 CAPLAN, GERALD. *Principles of Preventive Psychiatry.* New York, Basic Books, 1964.
4 HOLLINGSHEAD, AUGUST, AND REDLICH, FREDRICK. *Social Class and Mental Illness.* New York, Wiley, 1958.
5 IS MENTAL HEALTH A COMMUNIST PLOT? *S. K. & F. Psychiatric Reporter,* Sept.–Oct., 1962.
6 SZASZ, THOMAS. *Law, Liberty and Psychiatry.* New York, Macmillan, 1963.

II

COMMUNITY
PSYCHIATRY
IN
PRACTICE

Training for Community Psychiatry in a Psychoanalytically-oriented Department of Psychiatry

ISRAEL ZWERLING, M.D., PH.D.,
AND MILTON ROSENBAUM, M.D.

I T MUST surely take some special brand of courage to offer to tell a conference of colleagues how one goes about the training of residents in a subspecialty that the conference has just begun to define; but then many of us have been in the business of training physicians, psychologists, and psychiatric social workers to become psychotherapists, and we are certain that fully as fruitful a conference would result from a program identical to the present one but entitled "Psychotherapy: What It Is and What It Is Not." It is, indeed, discomforting to acknowledge that we are forced to take positions with reference to the training of specialists for work in a field we have not yet satisfactorily defined; perhaps this accounts for some of the heat with which we defend our positions. We would like to offer a brief working definition of community psychiatry as we view it, to describe our training program, and finally to report on some of the problems generated by the introduction of this program into our psychoanalytically-oriented residency training program.

We believe that community psychiatry can be defined in terms of four operational criteria. First, the subjects for study, diagnosis, and treatment tend to be population groups rather than individuals; second, the focus in etiologic formulations tends to be on conflict and disequilibrium in the significant social units of which the patients are members—the family, the parish, the schoolroom, the shop; third, treatment plans tend to be directed toward the broadest and most complete utilization of community resources; and fourth, effort tends to be invested in investigation, prevention, and rehabilitation rather than in diagnosis and treatment exclusively. Three crucial facts must be realized, however. First, not one of these criteria is unique to community psychiatry or absent from traditional, individual psychiatry; on the contrary, to a varying but considerable degree each represents a vital aspect of good traditional psychiatric practice, and each developed within the matrix of individual psychiatry. We will return to this point later. Second, each of the criteria must be integrated with, or added to, traditional individual practice. The observation was made in each of the four instances that community psychiatry represented a tendency to deal with population groups, to formulate etiology in terms of family and group dynamics, to utilize community resources in treatment, and to focus upon preventive and rehabilitative issues, and it tends in these directions from a baseline in individual psychology. We do not question the value of studying, for example, the contagious quality of panic in a large group, but, unless it is related to or integrated with some aspect of the intrapsychic dynamics of individual people, we consider it the province of the social psychologist rather than of the psychiatrist. Third, no one of the criteria is by itself a necessary and sufficient prerequisite for community psychiatry; all four must be present in an appropriate and meaningful pattern to constitute what we conceive to be the essence of a program of community psychiatry. At their extremes, community and individual psychiatry are readily differentiated— a weekly discussion group made up of mothers whose children have reading disabilities as opposed to the orthodox analysis of a patient with a character disorder. Between these extremes there is a large area of uncertainty, where the boundaries that separate community psychiatry from individual psychiatry are blurred and vague. We do not feel that it is important at this point to attempt a sharp differentiation between the two. We would sum up this effort at defining community psychiatry by suggesting that the actual techniques and areas of knowledge necessary for a community psychiatrist that are over and above those basic to the work of a traditional, analytically oriented psychiatrist include: (1) the dynamics of group process and group therapeutic techniques; (2) family diagnosis and treatment; (3) consultation to community agencies and institutions; and (4) the rudiments of epidemiology and community organization.

TRAINING

We provide two separate programs of training in community psychiatry in the Division of Social and Community Psychiatry— one that is offered in the general residency training program and is intended to provide the basic elements of community psychiatry in the training of analytically-oriented psychiatrists, and a more advanced curriculum that is offered in a post-residency fellowship program and is intended to train psychiatrists for the subspecialty of community psychiatry. We would like first to describe the former in some detail. Since this conference is focused on the general training of psychiatrists, we will describe the latter only briefly.

The general residency training program includes both didactic and clinical exercises. In the first year, two weekly didactic seminars are offered to all residents. One series is part of a continous three-year sequence on psychoanalytic theory and is entitled "Psychodynamics"—our residents refer to it as the "dream course." The other is divided into five sequences: orientation (two months); social and community psychiatry (four months); phenomenologic and descriptive psychiatry (two months); clinical psychology (one month); and neurophysiology (one month). The seminar sequence in social and community psychiatry begins with six sessions on group dynamics and group process; readings are assigned from the basic social psychology literature as well as from applied or clinical literature, and the resident training group itself is used as a focus for the observation of many of the group processes being discussed. These sessions are followed by ten seminars devoted to a review of some of the major contributions to epidemiologic studies and to the several levels of social determinants of behavior—family, community, social class, national, and cultural. (See the Appendix for the reading list used during the 1964 academic year.) Our experience this year, as in all previous years, is that these seminars are very well attended; the residents read the assigned material, discussions tend to be lively and even excited, and there is almost routinely a request that the series be extended, a request we must routinely refuse because of lack of time.

Clinical training in community psychiatry during the first year is largely centered in a four-month rotation in the Day Hospital Service, the 9:00 A.M. to 4:00 P.M. weekday hospital clinical service of the Division of Social and Community Psychiatry. We have described this service in two publications (5, 6). In brief, the Day Hospital is operated as a research service and admits acute psychiatric patients from a prescribed geographical area. Patients who are judged to require hospitalization by the admitting psychiatrist at the Bronx Municipal Hospital Center are then assigned in random sequence to the Day Hospital or the 24-hour In-Patient Service of the Department of Psychiatry. Since our residents are assigned during their first year to the In-Patient Service as well, this rotation is basically a continuation of the individual clinical work with psychiatric patients, but with the following exceptions:

1. Since patients reside at home evenings and weekends, their discussions tend to be about their lives in their communities and with their families. The nature of the relationships formed by patients to each other and to the staff tends to be quite different once the social forces at work in "total institutions" are no longer operative. Residents regularly observe that the hospital behavior of their patients while on the Day Hospital Service is "different."

2. For research purposes, it is a requirement of the Day Hospital Service that each patient, in addition to his individual treatment, be seen by his doctor in a weekly conjoint family interview. To support this clinical work, residents on the Day Hospital Service participate in a weekly family therapy seminar. This has rapidly become one of the most popular seminars in the

Division. Two initial sessions devoted to a review of the literature are followed by eight sessions in which the residents, through the one-way screen, observe one of the senior staff treating the family of a patient newly admitted to the Day Hospital. Each treatment session is followed by a discussion. Each of the residents in turn then meets under observation with one of the families he is treating. During the entire three-year general residency training period, each resident is assigned to two staff members with whom he discusses his patients in individual supervisory conferences; during the rotation on the Day Hospital Service, an additional hour of supervision is provided for family therapy.

3. Day Hospital patients are assigned to activity groups. There are three groups of up to ten patients each, and each group has a special group doctor, an activity leader (a nurse), an aide, and the part-time services of a psychiatric social worker. Groups meet at the start and the close of each hospital day, and group patients tend to spend a substantial part of each day together. Once each week the first-year residents observe and discuss a morning group meeting with a senior staff member of the Group Study Section of the Division. Most, though not all, first-year residents have some opportunity to serve as group doctors during their rotation. The residents also participate in weekly Group Process Rounds in which the week's events in each group and in the Day Hospital Service as a whole are reviewed.

4. Residents participate in the Division's continuous case seminar. The emphasis of this seminar, which follows patients for a two-month period, is interrelationships between the dynamics of the individual, his family, and his small group.

5. Residents attend the weekly Division staff meeting, at which work in progress in the Division is discussed. Although no effort is made to cover specific areas, the scope of the Division's work is so broad that material in all major areas of community psychiatry is certain to be presented in the course of a four-month rotation.

One additional facet of the training program for first-year residents merits comment. Four years ago there was a sharp difference between the clinical programs of the Day Hospital Service, and the In-Patient Service. On the former, interviews with patients' families were scheduled regularly and on the latter, they were avoided; on the former, group formative processes were facilitated and studied and on the latter, they were ignored; on the former, the concept of a patient-staff community was fostered and on the latter, informal role relationships (*i.e.* outside of those specifically prescribed by the doctor) between staff and patients were actively discouraged. Now, as a result partly of a change in the In-Patient Service leadership and partly of pressure from residents returning to the In-Patient Service following a rotation on the Day Hospital Service, this difference has largely disappeared. Patients on the In-Patient Service are organized into teams that function in much the same way as do the activity groups on the Day Hospital Service; therapeutic community meetings are held on the In-Patient Service as well as on the Day Hospital Service. While families are not seen in regularly scheduled treatment sessions on the In-Patient Service, they are seen routinely as part of each patient's intake processing, and the director of the In-Patient Service himself conducts a weekly seminar for the first-year residents in which he interviews the family of a patient. Thus, first-year residents gain experience in family behavior dynamics throughout their program, and not just during their period of rotation on the Day Hospital Service.*

* There has been a change in the residency training program since the presentation of this paper in 1964. First-year residents no longer rotate through the Day Hospital Service. The Day Hospital continues to function as described, but is staffed by residents and Fellows engaged in a two-year social psychiatry program at the third- and fourth-year or the fourth- and fifth-year levels. Several factors have contributed to this change: (1) the priority of other service and training needs in the limited time available in the first year of residency; (2) the unresolved question whether training in social and community psychiatry should occur in the first or in the third year of residency; (3) the growing similarity between the Day Hospital and the In-Patient Services in emphasis upon group process and family therapy, reducing the need for training in the Day Hospital during the first year of residency; (4) the struggle within the Department of Psychiatry between proponents of individual psychiatry and community psychiatry; (5) the introduction in the first year of residency training of weekly seminars in family dynamics and family therapy and in group process, reducing the need for this specialized training in these treatment modalities in the Day Hospital Service.

There is general consensus that Day Hospital training is valuable: at what point psychiatric residents should have this training in our program remains an open question. The answer largely depends upon the current administrative and service needs of a given institution. Thus an institution emphasizing long-term psychotherapy with highly selected private patients would probably not resolve the question in the way that an acute municipal psychiatric center would.

In the second year of general residency training there are two foci of training related to community psychiatry: a study of formal group psychotherapy and experience in our Walk-In Clinic. One trimester of non-analytic conference sequence is devoted to the teaching of formal group psychotherapy. After two initial sessions devoted to a review of the literature, the residents observe a trained group therapist conducting a sequence of treatment sessions with an outpatient therapy group. Two of the teaching techniques used in this program deserve mention: another trained group therapist observes the therapy group with the residents and comments during the session as well as in the discussion that follows; also, during the session each resident has one or more specific assignments: he is to act as a co-therapist, to observe a particular patient in the group, or to observe a particular dyad or subgroup.

Our Walk-In Clinic, which is part of our outpatient Mental Hygiene Clinic, has been described in a number of publications (1, 2, 4). In this screening and brief therapy clinic, the effort is made to have a psychiatrist see every patient at the time he seeks outpatient help without an intervening intake work-up. The central purpose of this clinic is to provide our residents with supervised experience in the conduct of brief psychotherapy and in the management of acute psychiatric problems not requiring inpatient treatment. This therapy, which is limited to a maximum of six sessions scheduled at the discretion of the resident and his supervisor (a patient may, however, be referred on for long-term psychotherapy in the Mental Hygiene Clinic), tends to be crisis-oriented, to require diagnostic skill in both psychodynamic formulation and in the assessment of social determinants of stress, and to demand the fullest use of family and community resources in the planning and execution of treatment. Patently enough, this service falls in the borderland between community and individual psychiatry: which aspect is stressed more heavily in the resident's Walk-In Clinic training usually depends on the inclination of his supervisor.

The third year of residency training is an elective year for our residents. All work for part of their time in the outpatient Mental Hygiene Clinic treating long-term psychotherapy cases. The principal assignments vary: two residents are appointed Chief

Residents; others may be appointed Research, Child Psychiatry, or Social Psychiatry Fellows; still others may elect to spend the additional time in the Mental Hygiene Clinic or on the adult In-Patient Service.*

Since we interpret our assignment for this conference to be the description of the training in community psychiatry we offer to general residents, we will mention only briefly the training of advanced residents and Fellows for specialization in this field. This training is evolving into a two-year program at the third- and fourth-year or at the fourth- and fifth-year levels. Until 1964, specific clinical assignments varied according to the research needs of our Division of Social and Community Psychiatry. Beginning in 1965, there will be formal didactic teaching in research methods, epidemiology, community organization, principles of social psychiatry, and family and group process; there will concurrently be supervised clinical experience on the Preventive Service, the Community Consultation and Diagnostic Service, the Day Hospital Service, and the Rehabilitation Service. The Preventive Service will be engaged in two major projects: the assessment of development in the children of psychotic parents; and the evaluation of the relative effectiveness of orthogenic-educational and psychiatric group techniques with parents and with teachers in the handling of early behavior disorders in elementary school children. The Consultation and Diagnostic Service will be offering consultation services at the start of each academic year to groups of public health nurses, the clergy, the Youth Investigations Unit of the Police Department, and the Bureau of Attendance Teachers, and will probably provide these services to one or two additional community agencies in the course of the year. The Rehabilitation Service began its preliminary study of the factors related to stabilization of the post-hospitalization recovery state by evaluating the effectiveness of a part-time work-for-pay program for severely disabled discharged

---

* Since 1964 third-year residents either participate in the two-year Social Psychiatry Fellowship program described in the text below, or, as part of the regular residency training program, they rotate for a four-month period through the Division of Social and Community Psychiatry, receiving training in community agency consultation techniques and in group and family process.

patients; a most felicitous turn of events will make it possible to establish in 1965 a halfway house for twenty adult outpatients.

PROBLEMS

An extended discussion of the problems that attended the birth and infancy of the Division of Social and Community Psychiatry in our Department has been presented in a previous publication (3). This article was written after what had begun as quite modest and restrained debates flared into angry arguments with all the *ad hominem* accusations one might expect, accusations with generally enough truth in them (the accusers were trained behavioral scientists) to divert attention effectively from the real issues for considerable periods of time. We prepared our report when we felt that we had identified the processes at work with sufficient accuracy to warrant certain conclusions, which can be summarized as follows:

1. There are real differences in study methods, in basic and applied behavioral data, in the problems addressed, and in the solutions proffered between community psychiatry and individual psychiatry, differences that ultimately derive from the different levels of integration represented by social-system theory and by psychoanalytic theory. This is not to assert that either has primacy over the other: it is as meaningless to argue this issue as it is for a well established psychoanalytic department to dismiss community psychiatry or to engulf it as merely an extension of psychoanalysis.

2. We do not adequately understand the relationship between social and intrapsychic determinants of psychopathology, and there are therefore discontinuities between individual and community psychiatry. So long as illness is classified as "mental"— and not defined in terms of social pathology—the psychiatrist must ultimately deal with an individual mental apparatus. The community psychiatrist learns what he can about the incidence and prevalence pattern of a syndrome of disordered behavior and identifies the forces and counterforces in the family, small group, community, and social class and in the cultural values in conflict. He then shifts from social-system theory to psychoanalytic theory (or some alternative individual psychological theory) in order to

elucidate the character of the individual patient's disorder in a formulation that takes into account the genetic, topographic, and economic characteristics of the psychopathology.

3. The extent of the clinical value of community psychiatry is largely unknown. One of the crucial tasks before us is the development of techniques for the objective assessment of the utility of community psychiatric practices. Since the time spent in the study of epidemiology or in the development of skill in family treatment reduces the time available for the study of psychoanalytic theory or for the development of skill in individual psychotherapy, conflicts will necessarily arise between the psychoanalytic and the community psychiatric staffs; and since so little is known concerning the usefulness of much of the knowledge and techniques of community psychiatry, these conflicts will be settled largely on intuitive grounds, with irrational power elements playing variably significant roles.

4. The presence in divisions of community psychiatry of such specialists as sociologists, anthropologists, community organizers, and epidemiologists—all foreign to the traditional team of psychiatrist, psychologist, psychiatric social worker, and psychiatric nurse—tends to increase the tension between the two divisions. Paradoxically, tension also arises when the analytically trained psychiatrists on the senior staff of the community psychiatry unit begin to practice what they teach and see families in their private offices.

5. Another factor that lends fuel to the fires occasioned by the growth of a division of community psychiatry in an analytically-oriented department is the fact that the origin of much of the armamentarium of the community psychiatrist lies in the practices of the traditional psychiatrist. On the one hand, the community program may lay claim to having originated a technique that is familiar to the traditional psychiatrist. The latter, in turn, may argue that he has "always worked with families" and fail to grasp the qualitative difference between the extensive study of family members as part of the study of the individual patient and the study of the family itself as the unit of health or illness.

6. We feel that the only guarantee of a mature resolution of these conflicts lies in full and open discussion of the issues. Thus,

in our program, we will continue to vary the assignment schedules for residents at all levels and in all areas of training, in accordance with the consensus we reach in assessing the experiences of the previous year. An audience sufficiently concerned about these issues to have come from distant places to participate in these discussions must surely share our convictions that, in the training of psychiatrists, eternal vigilance is the price of progress.

References

1   COLEMAN, M. D. Problems in an emergency psychiatric clinic. *Ment. Hosp.*, May, 1960, p. 26.

2   COLEMAN, M. D., AND ZWERLING, I. The psychiatric emergency clinic. *Amer. J. Psychiat. 115*:980–84, 1959.

3   ROSENBAUM, M., AND ZWERLING, I. The impact of social psychiatry on a psychoanalytically-oriented department of psychiatry with emphasis on residency training. *A.M.A. Arch. Gen. Psychiat. 11*:31–39, 1964.

4   WILDER, J., AND COLEMAN, M. D. The "walk-in" psychiatric clinic: Some observations and follow-up. *Int. J. soc. Psychiat.*, 9:192–99, 1963. 1963.

5   ZWERLING, I., AND WILDER, J. "Day Hospital Treatment for Psychotic Patients." In *Current Psychiatric Therapies*, Vol. II, edited by J. Masserman. New York, Grune & Stratton, 1962.

6   ZWERLING, I., AND WILDER, J. An evaluation of the applicability of the day hospital in treatment of acutely disturbed patients. *Israel Ann. Psychiat. relat. Discipl. 2*:162–85, 1964.

Appendix

ALBERT EINSTEIN COLLEGE OF MEDICINE
OF YESHIVA UNIVERSITY

SCHEDULE OF DIDACTICE SEQUENCE IN SOCIAL PSYCHIATRY
FIRST-YEAR RESIDENTS
JANUARY–FEBRUARY 1964

Date	Topic	Assignment
January 7	The Field of Social Psychiatry	Erikson, E. "The Problem of Ego Identity." In *Identity and the Life Cycle*. New York, International Universities Press, 1959.
January 14	The Concepts of Mental Health and Mental Illness	Jahoda, Marie. *Current Concepts of Positive Mental Health*. New York, Basic Books, 1958.
		Szasz, Thomas. *The Myth of Mental Illness*. New York, Hoeber Harper, 1961.
January 21	Social Determinants of Behavior: I. Cultural Determinants	Opler, Marvin. *Culture, Psychiatry and Human Values*. Springfield, Illinois, Charles C. Thomas, 1956.
		Kluckhohn, Florence. *Variations in Value Orientations*. Evanston, Illinois, Row, Peterson, 1961.
January 28	Social Determinants of Behavior: II. Social Class Determinants	Hollingshead, A. B., and Redlich, F. C. *Social Class and Mental Illness*. New York, Wiley, 1958.
		Harrington, M. *The Other America: Poverty in the U.S.* New York, Macmillan, 1963.

Date	Topic	Assignment
February 4	Social Determinants of Behavior: III. Ethnic and National Determinants	Kardiner, A., and Oversay, L. *The Mark of Oppression.* New York, Norton, 1951.
		Clark, Kenneth, and Clark, Mamie. *Prejudice in Your Child.* Boston, Beacon Press, 1950.
February 11	Social Determinants of Behavior: IV. Community Determinants	Zobrowski, M., and Herzog, E. *Life Is With People.* New York, International Universities Press, 1952. Shocken Paperback, 1962.
		Seeley, J. R., Sim, R. A. and Loosley, E. W. *Crestwood Heights.* New York, Basic Books, 1956.
February 18	Social Determinants of Behavior: V. Family Determinants	Parsens, T., and Bales, R. F. *Family Socialization and Interaction Process.* Glencoe, Illinois, The Free Press, 1955.
February 25	Social Determinants of Behavior: VI. The Social Role of a Psychiatrist	Goffman, Erving. *"Characteristics of Total Institutions."* In *Asylum.* Garden City, N.Y., Doubleday, 1961.
		Stanton, A., and Schwartz, M. *The Mental Hospital.* New York, Basic Books, 1954.

Five

Community Psychiatry for a Million People

F. E. COBURN, M.D.

THE province of Saskatchewan is the middle of the three prairie provinces of Canada and lies immediately north of the states of North Dakota and Montana. Its area is as large as the state of Texas. The southern half of the province is wheat farming country; the northern half is pre-Cambrian granite dotted with lakes and is heavily forested. The far northern extreme extends into subarctic tundra. In the settled area in the south, which is approximately 400 miles from east to west and 335 miles from north to south, live 950,000 people: the largest single group are of British origin, but Russians, Ukrainians, Poles, Germans, French Canadians, Indians, and other racial groups form a sizable proportion of the population.

The psychiatric services in this province are under the Saskatchewan Department of Public Health and have had dynamic, progressive leadership since 1946 and the support of a sympathetic government. In 1946 the psychiatric facilities consisted of two fairly large, old-style mental hospitals, one at the extreme northwest and the other at the extreme southeast of the province. Apparently the idea was "out of mind, out of sight." In the last eighteen years there has been a tremendous expansion of services and a movement from the old custodial, isolated institution into therapy and the community. We now have two large mental hospitals, at North Battleford and at Weyburn, a 148-bed psychiatric center at Yorkton (the first of six to eight small hospitals envisaged under the Saskatchewan Plan), psychiatric wards in three general hospitals, two training schools for mental defectives, and twenty traveling and six stationary mental health clinics. In addition, there are outpatient, emergency, and home care programs at the University Hospital. One outstanding feature of Saskatchewan psychiatry is the quality of our nursing staff. The old mental hospital attendant has been replaced by well-trained, registered psychiatric nurses, the product of a three-year training course of high caliber. Their progressive and professional attitude toward patient care has made possible much of our progress. Another significant advance was the Mental Health Act of 1961, which made admission to mental hospitals no more difficult than admission to general hospitals. A very large proportion of our patients are now voluntary patients who enter the hospital in a perfectly informal manner. Patients can also be committed to the hospital on the certificate of two physicians, and many of these can acquire voluntary status after admission. A third small group of patients is sent to the mental hospitals by action of the court. Since it is impossible for me to detail all the advances and all the methods used throughout the province, I will limit my discussion to three institutions: the University Hospital Department of Psychiatry; Saskatchewan Hospital at Weyburn; and Yorkton Psychiatric Centre.

Until 1955, the University of Saskatchewan had offered only the first two years of medical education. Then the University Hospital, Saskatoon, was built, and the course was expanded to four years. An important part of the University Hospital is its Department of Psychiatry, which has a 39-bed ward, physically indistinguishable from any other ward, on the fifth floor of the hospital. Patients are housed in one-, two-, and four-bed rooms. There is a staff-patient ratio of approximately one to one, and one-third of the staff are student nurses who spend much of their time off the ward in classes. It is our boast at University Hospital that in this open, unlocked, tastefully furnished unit we can treat all types of mental illness successfully and without danger to the patient, the public, or hospital property. Since this ward is used in teaching nurses, medical students, and psychiatric residents, a wide spectrum of psychiatric illnesses must be represented in it, and it was early suspected that this might be affecting our admissions policy so that we were not, in fact, treating all types of illness. Since the inception of the ward, we have set aside a total of seven beds for emergencies. The rule is that we always accept emergency admissions arising from within the University Hospital or from the city of Saskatoon, which has a population of 110,000. These emergency cases must be disposed of within forty-eight hours either by discharge, by transfer to a regular bed, or by transfer to the Saskatchewan Hospital at North Battleford. It was suggested that by transferring patients to North Battleford and by having practitioners commit their Saskatoon patients directly to North Battleford, we were eliminating the type of patient we could not handle. We did not believe this to be so, but to test the proposition in 1961 we set up Project 89. Six beds were set aside at University Hospital for patients from Saskatoon committed to North Battleford either by a general practitioner or from our own emergency beds. Whenever such a committment occurred, it was necessary to get permission for admission from the superintendent of the North Battleford Hospital. If any of our six special beds were empty, the patient came to University Hospital; if not, he went to North Battleford. This program was continued for a year and a half, and it was found that the open general hospital ward was indeed capable of handling all types of mental patients. A comparison of Project 89 patients with those admitted by the usual procedure did, however, reveal some differences between them, confirming the criticism that our admissions policy had been selective. Of our admitted and treated patients—that is, those not transferred quickly from our emergency beds—between 97 and 98 per cent are discharged back into the community. The remainder are transferred to North Battleford, not because we cannot handle them, but because they require longer hospitalization than we can provide in our small ward with the rate of turnover that is necessary for teaching. The average stay on our ward is twenty-two days, and into thirty-nine beds we annually admit 700 patients, of which 335 are psychotic, 165 neurotic, and the balance pathological personalities, alcoholics, mental defectives, etc. In addition to the usual inpatient service, we operate a day-patient service for patients who live in the community and come into the hospital from one to five days a week. An occasional patient is treated as a night patient, working during the day in the community and sleeping in the hospital. The day-patient and night-patient categories are usually used temporarily as a step toward full community living. Since 1955 we have operated an outpatient department. At first this department was operated along traditional lines as a separate service with its own staff. After two years, however, the department was reorganized so that each consultant, with his resident and medical students, operated his own outpatient service. With the exception of emergency admissions, all admissions are recruited from outpatients. This provides continuity of care: the same team looks after the patient in the outpatient department, in the hospital, and later, back in the community. Hospitalization is regarded as only one phase of patient care, and care in the community is considered to be of equal if not greater importance. The number of patients seen in the psychiatric outpatient department at the University Hospital increased from 660 in 1956 to 976 in 1963.

In addition to providing a screening service for admissions to the hospital, the outpatient service fulfills two other roles. The first of these is to provide treatment for a small number of neurotic patients who are carried in psychotherapy. This role is strictly limited because of a small staff and heavy teaching committments. The second role is to act as a consultant to general practitioners. In the whole of Saskatchewan, there are only three private psychiatrists, and the psychiatric service's mental health clinics are heavily involved with psychotic patients. As a result, the treatment of neurotic patients is left largely to the general practitioner. We believe that this is as it should be, that with psychiatric consultation the general practitioner can and should look after the majority of neurotics in his practice. The physicians who have graduated in the past twenty years have received a type of psychiatric training that was not available to earlier graduates, and they are capable, with some help in difficult cases, of handling most of the neurotics they see. A few will have to be referred for treatments to private psychiatrists, mental health clinics, or psychiatric outpatient departments.

Since 1955, the University Hospital Department of Psychiatry has offered an emergency service. At first this was just an "on call" service to the resident staff in the hospital's emergency department, but the case load increased from 46 psychiatric emergencies in 1957 to 669 in 1963. Because of this drastic increase, the emergency service was reorganized in 1963 and now has its own permanent psychiatric consultant. It is usually staffed by this consultant, one psychiatric resident, and one medical student. After 5:30 P.M. it is manned by the duty consultant and the duty resident. Patients can be seen immediately at the University Hospital and, if necessary, in the two other general hospitals in Saskatoon or in their own homes. Eighty per cent of the patients are sent by their general practitioners, 10 per cent are sent by social agencies or the courts, and 10 per cent are unreferred "walk-ins."

The referring practitioner discusses the case with the consultant before the patient is seen; or, if he has neglected to do so, the consultant telephones him. The patient is seen by our resident or medical student, who confers with the emergency consultant, and a decision is made regarding disposition of the patient. This decision is communicated to the referring practitioner first by telephone and later by letter. Thirty-eight per cent of these emergency patients are admitted to emergency service beds: half of these are treated and sent home, and half go to Saskatchewan Hospital, North Battleford. Of those not admitted to emergency beds, 23 per cent are given short-term treatment by the emergency service or are referred to our regular outpatient service, and 39 per cent return to their general practitioner with our advice regarding treatment.

It is interesting to note that 40 per cent of these patients have had their presenting complaints for two years or more and 45 per cent are seen because of deterioration of chronic illness. Only 10 per cent are seen because of an acute new illness. In a large number of cases, the reason for a patient's referral to the emer-

gency service is increasing anxiety on the part of his family or
general practitioner rather than an acute emergency. Eighty per
cent of these patients are handled with the limited resources in
the community. It seems clear that they could all be handled in
this way, given a moderate increase in the number of beds
available.

This service, we think, provides an excellent teaching situation
for both medical students and residents. Here the students see the
types of emergencies that occur in general practice and learn
how to handle them. The residents must assess, diagnose, and
treat quickly—a change from the more leisurely pace of an
inpatient service or a continued treatment outpatient clinic.

Our small ward and our outpatient and emergency services
provide facilities in the community for the treatment of Saskatoon
residents whose cases cannot be handled entirely by the general
practitioners. We are now attempting to meet the community's
need for services for the psychiatric patient who has chronic or
residual symptoms or a recurrent mental disability with our
relatively new and still experimental home care program. The
program began operation in 1961, and in 1962 a carefully
controlled study was begun, supported by a grant from the
National Institute of Mental Health. At first we placed on home
care only patients who were discharged from our University
Hospital psychiatric ward. More recently, we have added patients recruited from the psychiatric outpatient clinics and from
the emergency service. We at first restricted the patient groups to
residents of Saskatoon, but residents of the Saskatoon Rural
Health Region of the Provincial Department of Public Health
have since been included.

When a consultant feels his patient would benefit from home
care, he puts the patient's name up for a conference with the
home care team. If the patient is found to meet the criteria for
such care, a coin is tossed and the patient is assigned either to
home care or to the control group. If he is assigned to the control
group, the consultant continues to treat him as if no home care
program existed. The case is, however, followed up by an
independent evaluator so that the control group and the home
care group can be compared. If the patient is assigned to the

home care group, the situation is discussed in a planning conference attended by the consultant, his resident, and the home care team, and plans for the patient are made. The home care team consists of the director of research, the chief of the home care service, the co-ordinator of home care, the social workers assigned to home care, home care nurses, the secretary, and, if possible, the patient's general practitioner. The home care team plans the care of each patient to answer his individual needs. This care may include visiting nurses, visiting homemaker services, social worker calls, domiciliary visits by the psychiatric resident, and the constant supervision of the general practitioner and psychiatric consultant.

The consultant retains responsibility for the patient but delegates it to the home care team, which reports to him on the patient's progress. He makes any changes in medication required for the patient's psychiatric condition, and the general practitioner looks after any concurrent physical difficulties. The program has handled approximately sixty-two cases to date. Of the seven that have had to be transferred to a mental hospital, all but one were either over the age of sixty-five or suffering from chronic brain syndrome.

We believe that a general hospital psychiatric service, by operating an emergency service, an outpatient department and inpatient service with day care and night care, and a home care program, can serve the total psychiatric needs of a community without creating chronic patients who have to be transferred to custodial care. Any failure to achieve this in Saskatoon can be attributed, we believe, to bed shortage rather than to any inherent deficiencies in the system.

SASKATCHEWAN HOSPITAL, WEYBURN

In recent years this Saskatchewan Hospital has changed its population tremendously, largely by increasing emphasis on community care. The census figures in Tables 5.1 and 5.2 speak for themselves.

The big change has come since 1962, when a new superintendent and clinical director were appointed and major administrative changes were made. The medical and social work staffs

TABLE 5.1

MOVEMENT OF PATIENTS, SASKATCHEWAN HOSPITAL, WEYBURN
(1954–1963)

Year	First Admission	Readmission	Discharge	Death	Transfer	In-hospital Census	Difference	On-register Census
1954 a	360	166	462	128	8	1,880		1,987
1955	418	263	674	143	27	1,784	− 96	1,826
1956	393	274	547	133	101	1,641	−143	1,719
1957	297	264	525	143	3	1,554	− 87	1,618
1958	321	293	498	117	4	1,575	+ 21	1,622
1959	398	249	516	129	12	1,544	− 31	1,626
1960	438	316	601	120	12	1,574	+ 30	1,657
1961	474	368	762	166	20	1,527	− 47	1,561
1962	423	409	653	159	8	1,478	− 49	1,574
1963	390	327	679	188	7	1,202	−276	1,417

a Base year.

TABLE 5.2

ADMISSIONS, SASKATCHEWAN HOSPITAL, WEYBURN
(January 1963 to May 1964)

1963	First Admissions	Re-admissions	In-hospital Census	On-register Census
January	36	33	1,519	1,589
February	38	17	1,484	1,565
March	44	36	1,470	1,574
April	42	36	1,442	1,573
May	36	24	1,393	1,555
June	29	30	1,378	1,554
July	45	27	1,379	1,571
August	26	28	1,340	1,559
September	28	22	1,315	1,521
October	31	26	1,309	1,504
November	21	32	1,287	1,457
December	14	16	1,201	1,417
1964				
January	20	22	1,199	1,382
February	25	20	1,155	1,339
March	24	10	1,115	1,297
April	28	18	1,045	1,266
May	−	−	984	−

were assigned to regions of the hospital's catchment area. A team consisting of one psychiatrist and one social worker was made responsible for all the psychiatric work of one region: for the mental health clinics; for the screening of admissions; for the care of patients who were admitted; for arranging the discharge of these patients; and for their care in the community after discharge.

The regionalization program was begun in January, 1963, with the Weyburn-Estevan region. During the first six months of the program, admissions and readmissions were reduced by 30 per cent. By September, 1963, the whole area was regionalized, and at the same time certain internal reorganization was carried out in the hospital.

One hundred and ten beds were set aside as a "sealed" admission unit for all patients under sixty-five. No patient was to be transferred to a chronic unit from this admission unit, and none have been. This 110-bed unit serves a catchment area of 420,000 people, and it is rare for a patient to stay in the unit for more than three months. Patients over sixty-five are admitted to a geriatric unit; if found to have no organic disease, they are transferred to the 110-bed unit.

There are two geriatric units: one for newly admitted patients over sixty-five with organic disease; and one for patients with chronic illnesses who have grown old in the hospital. There is no build-up of long-term cases in the unit for newly-admitted patients, because the mortality is high and keeps pace with the admission rate (see Table 5.3).

Many of the patients in the chronic geriatric unit, a large proportion of them "burned out" schizophrenics, have been in the hospital for from twenty to forty years. It has been found that these patients, who are quiet and cause no trouble, do extremely well in old people's homes and nursing homes. In Canada, where there is an old age pension of $75 a month, they are usually able to finance themselves. Since Saskatchewan mental hospitals make no charges either to patients or to their families, many patients have let their pensions accumulate for several years. The hospital at Weyburn, which provides any necessary follow-up community services, has no trouble placing these patients in homes.

A vigorous program of social upgrading and industrial therapy has been instituted for patients under sixty-five suffering from functional psychoses. Patients are no longer used in institutional jobs unless such work is prescribed for therapeutic reasons: the institutional work must help fit the patient for work outside the institution. In addition, a number of subcontracts have been obtained from industrial concerns, and patients placed on this type of work are paid at rates varying from eight cents to a dollar per hour depending on the type of work and the patient's pro-

TABLE 5.3

MOVEMENTS OF PATIENTS AGED 65 AND OVER
Saskatchewan Hospital, Weyburn (1954–1963)

Year	Admissions	Releases	Deaths	Difference
1954	146	70	95	−19
1955	160	100	115	−55
1956	151	61	104	−14
1957	117	62	113	−58
1958	156	52	99	+ 5
1959	175	80	110	−15
1960	175	85	99	− 9
1961	175	76	139	−40
1962	209	71	136	+ 2
1963	186	113	164	−91

ductivity. An elaborate 13-point rating scale has been devised to measure the patient's socialization, self care, and industrial productivity. The patient's position on this scale determines the amount of pay he receives, the number of comforts provided him, the amount of freedom of movement he is allowed, and the amount of recreational activity he can participate in. These privileges appear to be effective motivating factors, and on some of the chronic wards all but one or two patients will be employed. As the patient moves up the 13-point scale, he receives more money and more privileges; when he reaches the top of the scale, he moves out of the hospital, possibly into a halfway house or boarding-out placement. This placement is thought of as temporary, and from it the patient moves on either into employment or into some form of social aid in the community, where his progress will be followed by his region's psychiatric team. This system is very flexible, however. A patient may work in the community and come back to the hospital to sleep, or he may live in the community and come back to the hospital to work, whichever seems to fit the requirements of his particular situation.

Fairly extensive use of psychotropic drugs, especially the phenothiazines, seems to be important in these programs. Patients who have had to return to the hospital have often been found to have discontinued their medication. Another interesting fact noted at Weyburn was that a certain group of patients had, in the past, had longer than average stays in the hospital and had produced more chronic cases. This group consisted of patients who spoke little or no English or were of an unusual religious affiliation, neither Protestant nor Roman Catholic. These patients were placed in a ward to which staff members with special linguistic abilities were assigned, and arrangements were made with the Canadian Mental Health Association to recruit volunteer visitors who could talk to patients who spoke languages of which the regular staff had no knowledge. Results, in terms of discharge, have been most encouraging.

While changes in hospital intramural programs have made possible an enormous increase in the number of patients discharged, this alone does not explain the over-all reduction in hospital population that has occurred since 1962. The increase in discharges might well have been reflected in a greatly increased rate of readmission. That this has not occurred and that, in fact, the readmission rate has fallen may be attributed to a vigorous mental health clinic program. There are fixed mental health clinics at Swift Current, Regina, and Moose Jaw, and traveling clinics at Weyburn, Estevan, Gravelbourg, Assiniboia, Wolseley, and Grenfell. In addition, there is a 25-bed psychiatric ward in Moose Jaw Union Hospital and a 53-bed ward at Regina General Hospital.

In the mental health clinics, top priority is given to the treatment of psychotic patients and second priority to those with personality and neurotic problems. Here, as at University Hospital, consultation with the general practitioner is a major function, and a relatively small number of patients are taken into individual psychotherapy.

The staff at Weyburn anticipates that their census will eventually level out at about 750, including 150 severe mental defectives—a legacy of the past when mental defectives were housed at Weyburn. Thus it appears that all psychotic cases occurring in a population of 420,000 can be handled by a system of psychiatric care consisting of a 600-bed mental hospital, two general hospital psychiatric units operating on a regional basis, and adequate community mental health clinics.

YORKTON PSYCHIATRIC CENTER

Since 1955, the Provincial Psychiatric Service has been advocating the Saskatchewan Plan for psychiatric patients. This envisioned the building of six to eight small psychiatric centers adjacent to general hospitals, each center to serve the total psychiatric needs of its designated area. There has been some debate over whether these centers should be separate institutions adjacent to general hospitals and sharing some of their services or whether they should be integral parts of the general hospitals. Aside from this minor point, there has been widespread acceptance of the Saskatchewan Plan throughout the province.

The first of these centers has been built at Yorkton, Saskatchewan. In 1961 a fixed mental health clinic was set up as the first step toward the center, and a small unit of eleven beds was obtained in the Yorkton Union Hospital in 1962. In October, 1963, the first unit of the Yorkton Psychiatric Centre was opened, and there are now forty-two beds open of a total of 148. But providing beds is only a small part of the function of the psychiatric center, as the Yorkton superintendent has stressed. What is needed is psychiatrists and social workers who can take their services to the community.

The area served by the Yorkton center is roughly 90 by 110 miles—larger than the state of Massachusetts or of Connecticut —with a population of 90,000. This area is broken down into six regions, much as the Weyburn area is, and each region is to be served by one psychiatrist and one social worker. These teams will look after all the psychiatric problems in their areas, holding mental health clinics where necessary and doing domiciliary visiting. While it is not economical for the psychiatrist to do much domiciliary visiting, he will go when, in the social worker's opinion, he is needed. The social worker will do most of the visiting, either as a follow-up of patients previously treated or at the request of the local general practitioner.

The Yorkton area has now been "sealed": no patients from that area are to go to other psychiatric facilities, and the Yorkton Psychiatric Centre must look after all the illness in the area. Since January, 1964, only one case—a medical legal patient who required close custody that Yorkton could not provide—has been sent from the Yorkton area to its parent mental hospital at Weyburn. In view of the fact that Weyburn has found 110 admitting beds to be adequate for a population of 420,000, there is reason to suspect that Yorkton will not need all of its 148 beds. The surplus can be used to advantage for cases requiring nursing home care.

I have presented here only a brief outline of the developments in Saskatchewan in the care of psychiatric patients, and I hope it will be useful to my American colleagues, who appear to be on the verge of a significant break-through in community psychiatry. I have some fears regarding these new developments, however. One is that they tend to stress neurotic, personality, and behavior difficulties to the relative exclusion of psychotic problems. Should we aim our major efforts at cure and treatment of the common cold, or at malaria, pellagra, cancer, and arteriosclerosis? The number of neurotic patients is almost limitless and treatment is long. With the limited number of professional people available, the community mental health clinic that stresses the treatment of minor illnesses soon becomes clogged, develops a long waiting list, and is unable to devote the necessary time and energy to our major psychiatric problems, the psychotic patients.

Community mental health centers should not be administratively or functionally separate from the state mental hospital system. In the patient's interest, it is imperative that we recognize that hospitalization is only one of the weapons for fighting mental illness, and one that, in the past, has been overemphasized. If the mental hospital is separately organized and operated, there is no possibility for continuity between hospital care and treatment in the community. Having community facilities under one administration and hospital facilities under another will lead to difficulties of communication which in my experience are almost insuperable.

The role of the family doctor in the care of the mentally ill must not be neglected. The patient should remain his responsibility and should not be taken over by mental health agencies. The family doctor should receive reports of patients' visits to a center immediately, preferably by telephone. Any changes in medication should be relayed to him, and in the intervals between clinic visits, he should assume responsibility for renewing prescriptions, checking on side effects of medication, monitoring the patient's condition, and arranging for community services as he sees they are needed.

For the past century, mental patients have been segregated in the mental hospital from general medical progress. They must not now become segregated in closed shop community mental health organizations. The demands on the community mental health center can be greatly reduced by utilizing the general practitioner, and the patient's interests are best served when the general practitioner can detect early changes in condition and alter treatment accordingly. This can and will be done if the general practitioner feels that he has the support of the mental health center for consultation and for emergency treatment. Psychiatry must re-enter the mainstream of North American medicine if it is to share in the benefits of the progress of medical science.

Finally, the community mental health organization should operate out of a general hospital. We should not have separate facilities for the treatment of the chest, the abdomen, the limbs, and the mind. The concept of the unity of the individual in which the mind and body are only technical, semantic abstractions is well accepted. We must not return to the dichotomy of the past, which has resulted so terribly in the inferior status of the mentally ill.

Six

Developing a Comprehensive Mental Health Program in a Metropolitan Community

ROBERT H. BARNES, M.D.

D URING this decade, the United States will see a major expansion of community mental health programs. This era of rapid growth has been catalyzed by the final report of the Joint Commission on Mental Illness and Health, *Action for Mental Health,* published in 1961 (5). Legislation passed by Congress late in 1963 promises to place substantial federal funds directly into local programs, initially for construction and very likely ultimately for staffing (7).

The services that may be rendered by community mental health centers are spelled out in considerable detail in the regulations drawn up by the Secretary of Health, Education, and Welfare to administer Public Law 88–164 (3), but the states will undoubtedly be allowed considerable leeway in developing their own plans and the communities in devising fiscal, clinical, and administrative patterns for local operations. The Greater Kansas City Mental Health Foundation, the basic public mental health authority in this large American city, represents one community's solution to the administrative, fiscal, and programmatic challenges we are now facing. (A detailed description of the Kansas City,

Missouri, development will be presented in a forthcoming Foundation book, *A Community Concern* [2].)

HISTORICAL DEVELOPMENT

A review of mental health and psychiatric facilities in Kansas City at the end of World War II presented a rather dismal picture. There was little concerted community effort to deal with the problems of mental health and illness in the area. Like other large metropolitan areas, Kansas City was faced with an increasing growth rate and the in-migration of large numbers of economically and socially deprived and marginal people from adjacent rural areas and from the South. Socio-economic factors, new understanding of mental illness, more optimism about treatment, and increasing interest from lay groups who saw delinquency and other aberrant behavior as psychiatric problems combined to create an increased demand for psychiatric and mental health services.

About this time several small, local charities federated to form the Kansas City Association of Trusts and Foundations, making available approximately one-half million dollars a year for basic health and welfare developments in Kansas City. One of the first areas selected for study was mental health. Dr. Jules Coleman, then professor of psychiatry at the University of Colorado, conducted an extensive survey and drew up specific recommendations under a grant from the new Association. As a result of his report and of further studies carried out by the Council of Social Agencies, over-all planning and an appraisal of needs was possible. The studies had noted the importance of combining public and private interests in the mental health field to provide a comprehensive program without overlapping of services. The Association of Trusts and Foundations took the lead in promoting these developments, despite the fact that many of the Association's trustees felt it was very risky to do business with local government agencies. A number of the professionals in city government were equally apprehensive about any kind of federation involving private funds that might interfere with the direct accountability of public funds. Despite reservations on both sides, however, a new organization, The Greater Kansas City Mental

Health Foundation, was incorporated under Missouri laws on May 25, 1950. At that time it received an initial grant of $350,000 from the parent Kansas City Association of Trusts and Foundations. The following month a contract was signed between the newly created Mental Health Foundation and the city of Kansas City. Under this contract the city was to develop a 70-bed psychiatric hospital, to be placed on the grounds of the city general hospital system and to be operated professionally by the Foundation. A number of contracts between the Mental Health Foundation and the city council have since been signed. There has been a tendency, as mutual trust has developed, for the city government to turn over more and more responsibility to the Foundation.

During its early years, the Foundation was also developing relations with and incorporating other agencies. The Kansas City Child Guidance Clinic was incorporated as the Foundation's Department of Child Psychiatry in 1953, and soon thereafter began to serve the Kansas City public schools through a contractual arrangement providing diagnostic, consulting, and therapeutic services to emotionally disturbed school children. Beginning in 1958, similar services were arranged with the three Jackson County institutions for delinquent children.

The success of the psychiatric program during its first eleven years stood out in marked contrast to that of other programs in the municipal hospitals, and in 1961 it was decided to develop a similar private, non-profit organization to assume operation of the entire city hospital system. It was hoped that this would stabilize the deteriorating medical care and training program on "hospital hill" and bring in new personnel, new programs, and new sources of financial support. In the spring of 1962 a private non-profit board was established, and to date it has had remarkable success.

CURRENT SERVICES

The Mental Health Foundation is today responsible for programs whose annual budgets exceed $1 million. Base financing from the Kansas City Association of Trusts and Foundations has been stabilized at between $60,000 and $70,000 a year to cover new developments and also to provide for certain administrative costs that are not readily supportable from public funds. Additional support for specific new projects has also been available from the Association. Currently, $50,000 per year comes from the Community Chest. All remaining funds, approximately $900,000 per year, are public funds from various units of government. The largest proportion of these funds comes from the city of Kansas City and the state Division of Mental Diseases, but substantial funds come as well from the local school district, the county government, and the state Division of Health, as well as the United States Public Health Service. These various funds support a 73-bed inpatient acute treatment service for medically indigent persons residing in Kansas City; public outpatient services for adults in the same area; a 40-patient capacity day hospital; an aftercare clinic; child psychiatric outpatient services for the whole Community Chest collection area of a million and a quarter people; diagnostic and consulting services for delinquent children in county institutions and emotionally disturbed school children in the central school district of Kansas City; and various other consulting services to social agencies and child care institutions. In addition, the Foundation provides emergency and consulting services to the city general hospital and functions basically as the department of psychiatry of that institution. The Foundation also carries on extensive training and educational activities. A three-year residency program is operated in the field of adult psychiatry, and a two-year fellowship program in child psychiatry. Clerkships for junior and senior medical students from the University of Missouri are provided within the Foundation's structure. All the psychiatric training programs are affiliated with the University of Missouri. In addition, programs are carried on for clinical psychology interns, psychiatric social work trainees, student nurses, psychiatric attendants, police officers, etc. The Foundation conducts research and demonstration programs through its two special departments of prevention and research.

A crucial factor in mental health developments in Kansas City has been the concept of the private foundation serving as the basic public mental health authority. But what is particularly unique about a private organization receiving public funds and operating psychiatric services? Mental hygiene clinics have operated under lay boards for more than three decades in this country, and a number of progressive states—Minnesota, Wisconsin, and New York are salient examples—offer matching funds to lay boards to operate community clinics (4). Medical schools and some general hospitals utilize public funds to operate services even though they are divorced from direct control by units of government.

The unique quality of the Kansas City experiment lies in its comprehensiveness and its basic program objectives. The Foundation attempts to tie together all of the basic psychiatric programs—service, training, and research—in a large metropolitan community. The Foundation program differs from university medical school programs in that, despite its deep commitment to training and education, its basic objectives are in the field of community mental health services. Although other organizational and governing devices obviously can and do work out satisfactorily, our experience in Kansas City indicates certain basic advantages in the private foundation approach, particularly if developmental capital can be made available to the foundation.

1. The private foundation allows for much greater flexibility in fiscal matters. Balances of certain funds can be carried over from one year to the next and at times transferred from one budget category to another, obviously within broad contractual limitations.

2. The structure of a private foundation permits more diversification of financial support than is possible with a government-administered program, and the result of this diversification is greater financial stability. The loss of one or more sources of income is less likely to be catastrophic. Further, the private foundation appears to be more successful in attracting support from other charitable funds and trusts.

3. Private foundation structure also makes possible much more flexibility in personnel management, including the establishment of salary ranges, the utilization of personnel, and the formulation of employee practices. Since it can provide special considerations, the private foundation is able to compete with industry and major universities for the services of particularly qualified people.

4. While employees are protected against unreasonable de-

mands by employee practice codes, management is able to exert a positive influence on personnel that is much more direct than a civil service merit system. The result is a higher degree of accountability of employees to management than exists in many governmental agencies.

5. Because the foundation is not a unit of local government, it is able to contract with different levels of government and essentially to federate public mental health activities and moneys with private funds. The result is a more effective program with fewer service duplications.

6. The foundation can set long-range programmatic goals and work toward them without the guidance and continual approval of higher levels that is frequently necessary in a governmental structure. Obviously, much of this broad programing must be sold to the contracting parties, a function which involves both the staff and the board of directors. Likewise, decision-making is accomplished more rapidly and with a minimum of checking upward. Program planning and fulfillment are facilitated because programs are not necessarily dependent on the enactment of enabling legislation.

7. Although the foundation must constantly deal with the political facts of life in local government, it is essentially out of politics and is not subject to the fiscal and political problems frequently encountered in agencies of local government. The board of a private foundation can act as a buffer, as has the board of our Mental Health Foundation, which has proved capable of managing pressures and of acting politically when necessary to assure the continuance and growth of the program.

8. There also appear to be advantages to the private foundation from the standpoint of employee morale and identification and community co-operation and pride. Certainly these are possible with agencies administered by a unit of government, but the average American apparently finds it easier to identify with and become enthusiastic about his work in a relatively small private setting than within a unit of similar size that is only part of a larger governmental whole.

These advantages, from the Kansas City experience of fourteen years, far offset the problems that occasionally arise in working with units of local government over questions such as control of funds and salary levels. In general these problems have been worked out amicably with reasonable assurances that public funds are being adequately and honestly administered.

GOALS AND OBJECTIVES

The development and the operation of every mental health center are influenced by goals and objectives, either explicitly spelled out by the administration or arrived at through experience and fed back into the decision-making and planning machinery. Goals for the Kansas City program have largely been derived from the experience of operating the enterprise and have, in time, changed.

In the clinical area our goals have changed significantly over the years. Initially the Foundation sought to operate a receiving center, caring for patients amenable to rapid psychiatric treatment and referring chronic cases elsewhere. For various reasons this goal proved unworkable. The state hospital system was unable for many years to accept any significant number of the chronically ill persons on referral or transfer, and the community was generally unwilling to accept this limited definition of function. The police department, private practitioners, and other referral sources were dissatisfied with the marked limitations in dealing with many of the chronic and severe behavioral problems that came to our doors. Many members of the staff were displeased by a policy that refused treatment to the people often most in need of help. Slowly goals were altered so that the major objective became the treatment of those whose need was most critical, from the standpoint of behavioral disturbance. Chronic illness and anticipated difficulty of treatment no longer excluded people from admission. These changes in goals were reflected in the Foundation's program: an aftercare clinic was established in 1959, and soon thereafter a day-hospital program. In the following years the function of the outpatient clinic was redefined, and its administration was consolidated with that of the inpatient services under one clinical director. One result of this move was to open up outpatient psychotherapeutic services to chronically ill dischargees from inpatient, day-care, and other services. It also necessitated the development in the outpatient department of extensive group therapy programs graded to the needs and the level of verbal sophistication of the patients. With the development of this array of closely integrated services, the diagnostic process became more crucial, and a centralized intake or screening clinic was developed to determine patient assignments to the various services.

In the educational area, the Foundation has taken on larger and larger training responsibilities. The basic goal in all these programs has been to equip the trainee with the theoretical knowledge and practical information necessary for serving the emotionally disturbed people he will encounter in practice. Our objective in training the psychiatric resident, for example, is to prepare him so that at the end of three years he will be capable of engaging effectively in the general practice of psychiatry on an independent basis. This objective assumes a comprehensive knowledge of psychopathology, psychodynamics, and the basic sciences that underlie psychiatry, as well as a mastery of the broad techniques of psychotherapy. In addition to this, however, the resident must be conversant with the skills and techniques of social and community psychiatry: small group techniques, group therapy, milieu therapy, ward administration, and family structure and therapy. The resident is also given broad instruction in community resources and in techniques of utilizing them so that he will be prepared, at the end of his three years of training, to undertake much of the responsibility for organizing and operating a comprehensive community program. He is encouraged to attain social and medical values that will allow him comfortably to care for chronically ill patients over long periods of time without feeling guilty or pressed by the necessity to take on only patients who can be "cured." The resident trained in this system —and to a considerable extent the psychologist, the social worker, and the nurse—must be able to break away from the more traditional concepts of his professional role. This transition is not always easy. Frequently the resident will feel that his position is inferior to that of the ward nurse. To attain a flexible view of his role—to learn to function as a strong yet unobtrusive leader, carrying the medical responsibility but allowing other disciplines to take the lead in areas of patient care where they are better equipped or more intimately associated with the patient—is indeed difficult. Some residents never advance to this stage and are unhappy with this aspect of their training. To them, training in psychotherapy during the second and third years comes as a welcome relief. Most residents, however, are able in time to make this adjustment and to equip themselves to operate effectively as team leaders in a community mental health setting.

Developments in the research area are important for stimulating clinical staff as well as for attracting and holding capable people—one of the more immediate goals of research development. Generally any type of project that is carefully thought out and can be conducted within the clinical and physical facilities of the institution is encouraged. Philosophically, however, research of an operational nature is more central to the goals of the community program. The Foundation has undertaken projects to determine where patients come from, how they get to the facility, what happens to them in the facility, and what happens to them following their use of various services. The results of such studies are utilized in the administrative and clinical planning of Foundation activities and have a significant impact on existing and projected programs.

Goals are difficult to formulate in the area of prevention, at least at an operational level. The area of primary prevention is the issue here, since the Foundation in its clinical programs in both adult and child psychiatry is deeply concerned with secondary and tertiary prevention. The operational goal in the instance of primary prevention is to develop carefully controlled programs aimed at significantly lowering the incidence of emotional disturbances in the Kansas City region. It is interesting that at the Foundation most of the impetus for a prevention program came not from the professional staff but from the board and from co-operating agencies such as the school system and the mother trust, the Kansas City Association of Trusts and Foundations. The latter group made an initial grant of $25,000 to the Foundation in 1959 for preliminary development of a prevention program. The core of this development has been carried out in co-operation with the Kansas City School District, a large metropolitan system serving over 75,000 children. In 1961 a long-range project entitled the Kansas City, Missouri, School Behavior Project, financed by the National Institute of Mental Health, was undertaken in conjunction with the school system. This project has assisted teachers at the sixth grade level in managing behavioral disturbances within their own classrooms by providing specialized experience in group dynamics and other techniques in intensive summer courses and continuing seminars. Current plans are to continue this activity with teachers at other grade levels with the active, programmatic involvement of school principals. Other more ambitious and comprehensive prevention programs are currently being planned by the Department of Prevention, in cooperation with the Kansas City School District.

The subject of goals within the administrative area is an important one, but too involved for more than cursory treatment here. The Cummings, some ten years ago, pointed out the significance of this area in an article entitled "The Locus of Power in a Large Mental Hospital" (1). Administrative issues often receive relatively little attention from psychiatrists, and the Cummings article deals with some of the consequences of this fact. Lemkau has cogently reviewed this issue: "The challenge of administration is to fill the gap between the need for money and the need for services with a workable structure in the realm of the 'art of the possible.' Psychiatry cannot abhor the administrative vacuum, nor ignore its challenge; it must fill it or be displaced by someone or some group which does see the function of administration as the challenge to skill in human organization it presents" (6).

Many areas are involved in the administration of large community mental health programs. The problems of directing treatment in various services are in the province of ward administration. Many academic administrative problems arise in the planning and organization of educational programs. In these various areas a major goal has been to utilize a horizontal rather than a vertical pattern of organization, that is, to have decisions made as far down in the organizational hierarchy as possible. The results appear to be less resistance to administrative and organizational decisions, and the freeing of clinical personnel from many organizational duties.

At another level are the administrative problems related to budget and to fiscal planning and control, and to organization and supervision of supporting services such as maintenance, housekeeping, and food. At the Foundation the direct but not the ultimate responsibility in this area rests in a Department of Administration, headed by a director trained in public administration. The importance of this area of non-clinical, non-educational administration must not be underestimated. The goal in this area is to provide the best possible level of patient service. Efficient administrative procedures are a means to this end, but they must not be considered an end in themselves. It is often popular for the clinical group to consider themselves the "good guys," concerned only with patient welfare, and administrative people the "bad guys," concerned only with dollars and personal perogatives. Nothing is more destructive to the attainment of over-all institutional goals than this kind of division among staff members.

The experience at the Foundation, which parallels that reported by the Cummings (1), underlines the wisdom of placing the final administrative responsibility with the top medical administrator at the Foundation—the executive director, a psychiatrist. This may not be necessary, but it would seem to insure that patient and clinical needs have a reasonable chance at top priority. Constant formal and informal interaction between clinical staff and the Director of the Department of Administration further strengthens this priority. It is an interesting fact that the non-clinical administrator frequently develops procedures that are much more closely oriented toward patient welfare than those suggested by clinical staff.

The fiscal goal may be stated simply as the mobilization of sufficient funds to carry on the services indicated by the other goals of the Foundation. This has meant developing many sources of support and consolidating them under a unitary administrative and fiscal system. The professional staff, in attempting to develop the most effective services at the least cost to the public, has been constantly aware of the increasing tax burden imposed on the local community by the development of adequate mental health services. Broadening the base of support has prevented the organization from being totally dependent on any one group and thus faced with disaster by a withdrawal of funds from any single source. There has been a continuing effort to increase the level of support from patient fees and from all the units of local government as well as from federal, state, and private grant sources. The goal of economic viability may seem too apparent to be elaborated, but, unless it is kept constantly in mind, the whole enterprise is in chronic jeopardy, and new program developments are impossible.

FUTURE PLANS AND PROBLEMS

The Division of Mental Diseases of the State of Missouri has recently acquired the facility across the street from the Psychiatric Receiving Center, and the Foundation is currently working out contractual agreements with the state in order to add to its current services the facilities of this 120-bed acute treatment center and its associated day-hospital and outpatient services. The Foundation, in conjunction with the Division of Mental Diseases, will then serve the western third of Missouri. This plan will more than double the staff and budgets of the psychiatric services, and contractual arrangements are being worked out which will allow basic program and professional direction to reside with the private Foundation.

Another major development involves the association of the Foundation with the new private corporation that operates the city general hospital system. The long-term objective of this comprehensive medical center is to develop a major medical training institution in Kansas City, eventually culminating in the establishment of a four-year medical school.

At the present time, the Mental Health Foundation is the basic public mental health authority in Kansas City, providing community mental health services to a large portion of the metropolitan area, and it will soon co-operatively operate a unit of the state hospital system. It is also the department of psychiatry of a newly developing medical center. The major problem facing the Foundation is that of maintaining comprehensive community mental health services while at the same time becoming increasingly involved with development of a major university medical teaching center and with the service functions of the state hospital system. The Foundation believes that it can keep these three programs in reasonable balance and that the community mental health programs will not suffer. Whether the Foundation can successfully exercise its control over these developments, however, remains to be seen.

References

1   CUMMING, J., AND CUMMING, E. The locus of power in a large mental hospital. *Psychiatry 19*:361, 1956.
2   EPPS, R., BARNES, R., AND McPARTLAND, T. *A Community Concern.* Springfield, Illinois, Charles Thomas, 1965.
3   GRANTS FOR CONSTRUCTION OF COMMUNITY MENTAL HEALTH CENTERS, 42 C.F.R., Part 54, Subpart C (1965 Supp.).
4   HIGHLIGHTS OF RECENT COMMUNITY MENTAL HEALTH LEGISLATION. Joint Information Service, American Psychiatric Association and National Association for Mental Health. *Fact Sheet,* No. 8, Jan., 1959.
5   JOINT COMMISSION ON MENTAL ILLNESS AND HEALTH. *Action for Mental Health.* New York, Basic Books, 1961.
6   LEMKAU, P. The relation between money and services. *Amer. J. Psychiat. 119*:1182, 1963.
7   MENTAL RETARDATION FACILITIES AND COMMUNITY MENTAL HEALTH CENTERS CONSTRUCTION ACT, 77 Stat. 282(1963), 20 USC § 611–613, 617–618, 676; 42 USC § 291k, 259–295e, 2661–2665, 2671–2677, 2681–2687, 2691–2696.

Seven

The Ideational Basis of a State Program for Community Mental Health Services

H. G. WHITTINGTON, M.D.

THE public administrator lives in a world divided between political expediency and professional premeditation. While he sometimes continues to pursue the ideal, he repeatedly settles for the attainable. The social climate in government—at least in state and local governments—is decidedly anti-intellectual and to some extent even antiprofessional. Opportunism is the order of the day, and action at all times transcends introspection.

The task of the public mental health administrator, particularly in community mental health activities, is further complicated because he deals with a heterogeneous system of agencies and services. The result is a fragmentation of authority greater than the fragmentation of responsibility: the director of a community mental health service tends to be given a larger proportion of responsibility for the state community mental health program than he is given authority to implement changes or improvements.

In the comments that follow, I will try to demonstrate the attempts in one specific state—Kansas—to cope with these forces, as well as with the professional and scientific issues involved in the largely unexplored areas of community mental health.

NOTE: At the time this paper was presented, the author was Director of Community Mental Health Services for Kansas.

THE KANSAS SITUATION

Kansas has a population of approximately 2,200,000 distributed over 82,264 square miles. This yields an average population density of only twenty-seven persons per square mile, a fact that must always be kept in mind in planning for services. In western Kansas the population distribution is even thinner: approximately 330,000 people live in an area of 40,000 square miles, resulting in an over-all population density of eight persons per square mile. In contrast, the Netherlands, with a total land area only a little over one-sixth that of Kansas, has five times the population.

Within this sparsely and unevenly distributed population, even greater discrepancies may be found. On a county-by-county basis, the population ranges from a low of 2,500 in a county of approximately 900 square miles to a high of 324,000 in the county with the highest population density—360 persons per square mile.

The guidelines for federal participation in the construction of community mental health centers state that in order to qualify as a comprehensive community mental health center a facility must serve at least 75,000 persons. In western Kansas this would mean that a comprehensive center would have to serve the population of an area of over 9,300 square miles. I will later indicate how we have attempted to deal with this problem in our planning.

Community mental health clinics are not very new in Kansas, or in other states; recent changes involve acceleration in the development of new centers, increasing diversification of services, and elaboration of orientation and philosophy. In reviewing the development of the community mental health program in Kansas, I will discuss some of our long-range plans—plans developed in part with the help of the federal grant for planning comprehensive mental health services; I will try to make explicit the assumptions upon which our program is built; and I will point out problems that have arisen and issues that remain unresolved.

THE HISTORY OF COMMUNITY MENTAL HEALTH SERVICES IN KANSAS

The Wichita Child Guidance Center opened in 1929, and, with the support of the United Fund, has operated primarily as a psychological clinic. The second clinic in Kansas was opened in Atchison in 1938. The remaining nineteen community mental health centers, however, have opened since World War II.

It was not until 1948 that Kansas took advantage of the funds made available by the National Mental Health Act of 1946. As the legislation was written, the State Board of Health, unless the state designated otherwise, became the mental health authority. Mental health professionals, however, including those involved in the state mental health program, displayed little interest in participating in the development of community mental health services. At that time, a revolution in the state hospital program was just beginning. Many changes came about during the next decade, such as the development of the Topeka State Hospital from a custodial institution with 1,700 patients, only 193 admissions a year, and a staff of eight physicians to an active treatment and training center with a population of 871, with 936 yearly admissions, and a staff of forty physicians.

The initial task of the community mental health program was to educate and involve the citizens of the state in the improvement of mental health services. The state mental health authority is only one of the forces responsible for the current high level of citizen awareness of and sophistication about mental health needs and services: the Menninger Foundation and related psychiatric institutions share much of the credit.

Centers based entirely upon local initiative, governed by citizen governing boards, and supported entirely by local tax funds began to develop, and the rate of development steadily increased. The development of these services has apparently followed the rules reported by the National Science Foundation as governing the diffusion of technological change (9). Many of these postulates concerning diffusion of technological change within an industry seem applicable to the diffusion of changes within the mental health industry. These hypotheses are as follows:

1. As the number of firms in an industry adopting an innovation increases, the probability of its adoption by a non-user increases.

2. The expected profitability of an innovation influences the probability of its adoption.

3. For equally profitable innovations, the probability of adoption tends to be smaller in the case of innovations requiring relatively large capital investment.

4. Probability of adoption is dependent on the industry in which the innovation is introduced.

5. If the innovation displaces very durable equipment, the probability of its adoption is lessened.

6. The probability of adoption will be higher in firms that are expanding at a relatively rapid rate.

7. All other factors being equal, the probability of adoption increases with time.

In Kansas, as time has gone on, as the number of counties supporting a mental health center has increased, as the mental health industry itself has become more fluid and less static, and as the expansion rate of the mental health professions has increased, the development of community mental health centers has steadily accelerated. The innovation has been profitable and has required relatively small capital outlays. Anxiety has been increasingly aroused in recent years, however, concerning the displacement of durable equipment—in this instance the existing state hospital program—and this anxiety is presently exerting some dampening effect on the growth of community mental health services.

BELIEF SYSTEM

Until fairly recently, community mental health services in Kansas have been developed along the lines of the guidance center and have emphasized treatment services, primarily for children. In attempting to broaden this conceptual framework, however, we have arrived at eleven core beliefs, some of which cannot be proved with our present knowledge:

1. We believe that mental and emotional illness is the result of a complex and often imperfectly understood interplay between biological, social, and psychological events.

2. We believe that the individual cannot be fully understood or effectively helped unless the social context and interpersonal field

within which he lives, becomes ill, and recovers is understood.

3. We believe that the closer geographically, temporally, and socially the individual can be treated to the milieu in which he lives, the better. We are firmly committed to the concept of "battlefield psychiatry" (the belief that the home, the neighborhood, and the community are the psychological battlefield).

4. We believe that severe mental illness evolves from mild and moderate personal and social disability. While recognizing that some of the major psychoses have strong biological determinants, we believe that prompt recognition, early and effective treatment, and continuing care in the community can, in many cases, prevent decompensating psychotic states. Consequently, secondary prevention through case-finding and early treatment is a crucial link in our chain of services.

5. We believe that primary prevention of recognizable emotional illness is also possible, and that, in view of the growing body of knowledge concerning the participation of mental health consultants in primary prevention, programing and research in community mental health centers should utilize concepts of primary prevention (2).

6. We believe that local government should do only that which individual citizens cannot do for themselves; that state government should do only what local government cannot do; and that the federal government should do only what state government cannot do. Adherence to this philosophy has meant that citizens of the communities and counties of Kansas have consistently been given the opportunity to assume responsibility and exercise authority. To date, thirty-eight of the 105 counties of Kansas— containing approximately 67 per cent of the state's population— have assumed this responsibility and are exercising it with considerable wisdom and vigor.

7. We believe that, in mental health services, as in many aspects of our national life, there is an area for public enterprise and an area for private enterprise. We do not see community mental health services as supplanting or competing with private psychiatric practice; nor for that matter do we see local services as supplanting or competing with state or national services.

8. We believe that the prevention and treatment of illness and the promotion of mental health are not the property of any one group but of the total community.

9. However, we believe that the responsibility for leadership is essentially a medical and psychiatric one.

10. In the final analysis, we believe that those who are best suited to lead will lead. If psychiatrists are best fitted, both by training and by aptitude, to provide leadership in the community mental health field and are willing to accept the incumbent responsibilities, there are no doubts in my mind that they will rise to that leadership and responsibility as the years go by. If we in psychiatry are not able consistently to offer this leadership and to provide superior service within the context of the community, leadership will properly devolve into the hands of other professionals.

11. We believe that while each of the mental health disciplines can offer maximum help to a certain portion of the total spectrum of mental and emotional illnesses, the basic team of psychiatrist, clinical psychologist, and psychiatric social worker is necessary to meet most competently the needs of all patients.

Consequently, we have adopted as the minimal requirements for a comprehensive center serving a population base of at least 50,000 a staff consisting of a full-time psychiatrist, a clinical psychologist, and a psychiatric social worker, as well as a tax income of at least $40,000 per year.

WHAT DO COMMUNITY MENTAL HEALTH CENTERS DO IN KANSAS?

Each of the community mental health centers in Kansas serves at least two basic functions: provision of direct clinical services, and provision of consultative services to other community caregivers.

The amount of time spent in direct clinical services varies from 40 per cent to 90 per cent, depending upon the center. All of the centers except one serve both adults and children and evaluate and diagnose all mental and emotional disorders. Treatment activities consist of casework, casework therapy, counseling, psychotherapy of brief and moderate duration, group psychotherapy, group casework, and the use of appropriate medications. In addition, several centers have developed day activity programs utilizing professional and volunteer personnel, and a number, either independently or in collaboration with the local mental health association, have developed social clubs for patients returning to the community from state hospitals (4, 5, 6).

Our model for mental health consultation is essentially the consultee-centered consultation described by Gerald Caplan and his associates (3). The majority of the professionals working in community mental health centers have had no previous experience in consulting with community care-givers and, consequently, must learn this process through reading, through discussion with other staff members, and through the in-service training and consultation provided by our state-level staff. Consultation services are generally provided to county welfare departments (which in Kansas are involved in aftercare services for patients returning to the community from state hospitals), local school personnel, public health personnel, ministers, physicians, and the juvenile court.

The concept of mental health consultation has gradually found favor with the practitioners working in the centers and is now being accepted by the other care-givers within the community. We have consistently striven to make clear that the mental health center is part of the matrix of helping services within the community and does not come into the community to displace these services or to do away with the need for them, but rather to work in collaboration with them.

Community mental health centers have taken part in a variety of other non-clinical activities, such as the worry clinics conducted by the County Associations for Mental Health; preschool mental health roundups; suicide seminars; case-centered consultation to counseling and guidance services at colleges and universities; in-service training for school and other personnel; and training of psychiatric residents, clinical psychology interns, and social work students.

Each of the three general state psychiatric hospitals in Kansas is divided into four semiautonomous sections that serve designated counties, and the staffs of the mental health centers in the areas served by these sections are developing close working relationships with the section staffs. The result is improved communication, sharing of responsibility for patient care and predischarge and aftercare planning, and, in general, facilitation of continuity and comprehensiveness of care for the individual patient.

RESULTS

What has all this activity led to in our sparsely populated Midwestern state? Between April, 1961 and April, 1963, the total report of professional staff hours in public and private non-profit clinics in Kansas rose from 5,456 to 6,470 hours per week. This represents a 19 per cent increase, the greatest part of which occurred in centers supported by community mental health levies and administered by local mental health boards. By April, 1963, the level of total outpatient service in Kansas had reached 294 man-hours per 100,000 population per week, which was already in excess of the recommended Joint Commission level of one psychiatric team per 50,000 population. Despite this, there is a marked over-all shortage of outpatient services, and the existing services are largely concentrated in the northeast corner of the state. In addition to twenty-one community mental health centers, there are three general psychiatric outpatient clinics at the state hospitals, specialized outpatient clinics at other state institutions, and outpatient departments at the Menninger Foundation and at the University of Kansas Medical Center.

Between 1961 and 1963, professional staff time in community-supported centers alone increased from 1,670 to 2,280 hours per week, an increase of 37 per cent. From spring, 1963 to spring, 1964, staff hours per week increased 24 per cent to 2,821.

In January of 1962 there were fifteen counties levying a mental health tax; by January of 1964, the number had increased to thirty-eight, involving 67 per cent of the state's population.

By April of 1964, 2,821 man-hours per week were reported for centers serving 1,455,000 people, a level of service of over 190 man-hours per week per 100,000 population for the portion of the state with community-based services. The standard recommended by the Joint Commission on Mental Illness and Health—

105 hours per 50,000 population per week (7)—has almost been reached in these areas.

And yet nowhere are the needs for evaluation, treatment, and rehabilitation services, much less for preventive services, being adequately met.

ECHELONS OF SERVICE

Just as we have made the mistake of talking about mental illness as if it were one disease, we have erred in talking about community mental health centers as if they were all alike. It seems to me more appropriate to think in terms of echelons of service and of a "chain of evacuation" for psychiatric casualties from the community.

The first echelon of care includes the professionals who are already providing mental health services in the communities of Kansas. Their patients may not necessarily be defined as mentally or emotionally ill but may be described by the community as deviant, bad, criminal, or merely as having normal difficulties in living. Public health personnel, physicians, welfare workers, school psychologists, special education personnel, classroom teachers, juvenile and district judges, mental health associations, ministers, volunteer social agencies, and other individuals and groups are available to help those experiencing difficulties that might be labeled as incipient or early mental or emotional illness. These professional, non-psychiatric care-givers play particularly crucial roles in case-finding and referral for diagnosis, in crisis intervention, in providing psychiatric first aid, and in providing mental health education within the community. None of the subsequent echelons of service displaces the workers in the first echelon.

The majority of the mental health centers that have been developed in this country, and all but one of those in Kansas, fall essentially into the second echelon of care. In addition to providing basic psychiatric evaluation and outpatient treatment, these centers offer consultative services to first-echelon agencies and individuals. This second echelon of service could perhaps be compared to the regimental clearing station in the army, where patients are treated and either restored to duty or evacuated to more complex treatment facilities in the rear. Of the twenty-five community mental health centers planned for Kansas in the foreseeable future, approximately fourteen will fall in the category of second-echelon services. These facilities may be either medical or non-medical; and the psychiatrist may participate either as director, as consultant, or as a staff psychiatrist who is responsible only for the patients under his care.

Eleven of the community mental health centers have a potential for development into third-echelon facilities, which could be called comprehensive community mental health centers. These facilities, which might be likened in our military analogy to the field hospital, would also provide inpatient treatment, day-hospital services for children and adults, home treatment services, expanded consultation as well as mental health education services, rehabilitation and mental retardation services, and services for special groups such as alcoholics and patients returning from state hospitals.

Figure 7.1 indicates how the staff of an agency could be organized to provide this spectrum of services. The facility in question is clearly a medical one and should ideally be under the over-all direction of a fully qualified psychiatrist; at the least, its division of clinical services should be directed by a psychiatrist. In urban areas, where many services already exist, a new agency may not be needed. A mechanism for regional planning and co-ordination of services, such as that outlined in Figure 7.2, may be sufficient to insure comprehensive, available, and continuous services. Free movement of patients between agencies must also be insured.

Fourth-echelon facilities may be desirable in certain states. These are essentially the state-supported receiving or intensive-treatment units, often called psychiatric institutes, that offer evaluation and brief intensive treatment to the acutely ill. Most of these units are in urban areas, are affiliated with training and research centers, and are richly staffed and well financed.

In Kansas, however, the current policy is for each of the three state hospitals to remain a comprehensive psychiatric center, organized on the section plan, with the four semiautonomous units

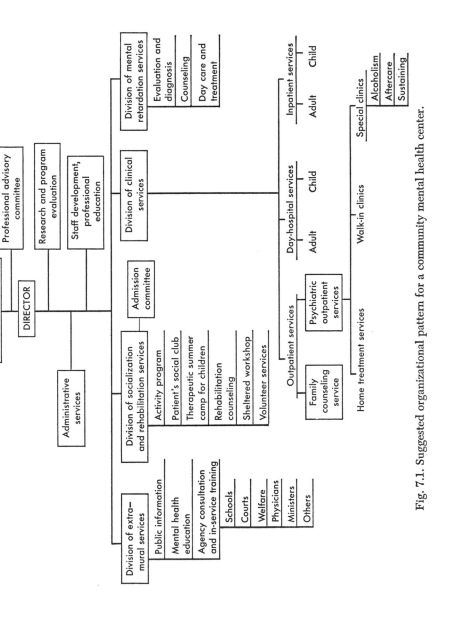

Fig. 7.1. Suggested organizational pattern for a community mental health center.

Fig. 7.2. Suggested organizational pattern for regional planning and co-ordination of services for mental health.

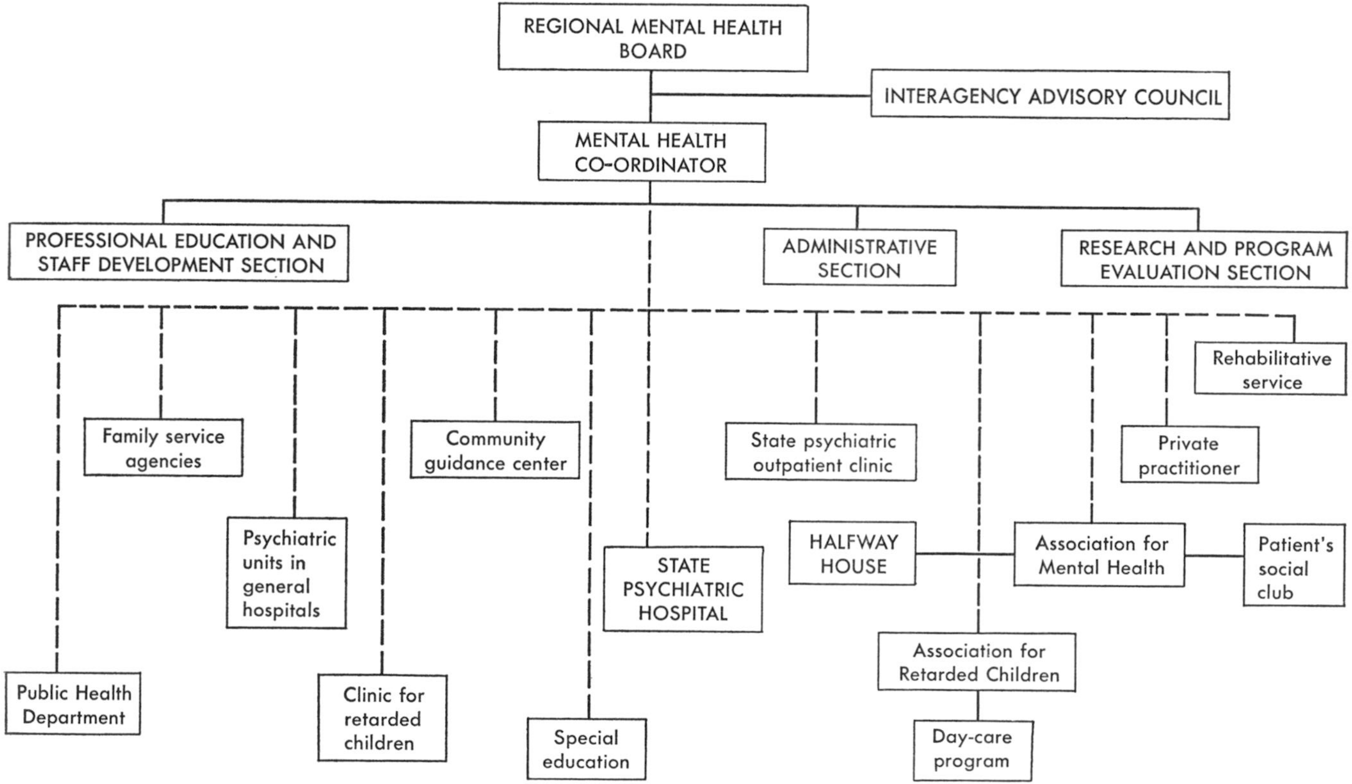

REGIONAL MENTAL HEALTH BOARD

INTERAGENCY ADVISORY COUNCIL

MENTAL HEALTH CO-ORDINATOR

RESEARCH AND PROGRAM EVALUATION SECTION

ADMINISTRATIVE SECTION

PROFESSIONAL EDUCATION AND STAFF DEVELOPMENT SECTION

Rehabilitative service

Private practitioner

Patient's social club

Association for Mental Health

Association for Retarded Children

Day-care program

State psychiatric outpatient clinic

HALFWAY HOUSE

STATE PSYCHIATRIC HOSPITAL

Special education

Community guidance center

Clinic for retarded children

Psychiatric units in general hospitals

Family service agencies

Public Health Department

in each hospital serving defined geographic areas. Each of these twelve sections will continue to offer the full spectrum of care for patients requiring hospitalization in a state facility. Diagnosis and treatment planning, intensive treatment, continued treatment, and rehabilitation will be carried on within each section. There is still some uncertainty about how the needs of special populations, such as children and adolescents, should be handled. At present children under sixteen are treated in separate facilities at a single state hospital. In an experiment being conducted at Osawatomie State Hospital, adolescent patients reside on the section serving their district but come together for a special treatment program on the grounds of the state hospital. This is essentially a day-hospital service for the hospital's adolescent population.

The state psychiatric hospitals in Kansas comprise a fifth echelon of care and are essentially residential psychiatric communities. The state hospitals are currently examining the possibility of providing, in addition to direct treatment services, consultation and in-service training to the second- and third-echelon mental health centers in Kansas. By developing this extramural aspect of the program, the state psychiatric hospital can play a vital role in comprehensive mental health services.

PROBLEMS

The rosy picture that has been presented in the preceding paragraphs is, of course, an oversimplification. Many problems, some of which will remain for years, have arisen, and few have been solved.

I need not remind you that the shortage of personnel is the most serious and irreconcilable of these problems. Our success in staffing certain of our programs has been the result of luring personnel from other states to Kansas. To some extent we are all still in the cannibalistic stage of development, and continued expansion of training programs in all of the mental health disciplines is urgently needed.

Other problems, however, deserve our attention here. The citizen governing board is a traditional and time-honored mechanism of our democratic society. However, such a board's capability to administer a community mental health center is by no means above doubt. The selection and composition of the governing board, while specified to some extent in our law, are matters requiring constant attention. Providing adequate in-service training for board members (in Kansas there are about one hundred new board members each year) is a serious problem for the state mental health authority. The weakness of the board system is most apparent in the area of personnel selection. Anyone who has spent time with citizen governing boards will have discovered that often their sole criteria for judging prospective personnel is "likeableness." They characteristically tend, if left entirely to their own devices, to employ personnel who are less trained, less assertive, less opinionated, and by and large less competent. The well-trained, determined, self-directed, and ambitious professional person will quite often be considered a threat by the governing board, who will manage to avoid employing him. This is a serious problem, and we have as yet achieved no entirely satisfactory solution.

Definite problems exist for the staff of the community mental health center as well. Just as the state hospital tends to attract persons with strong dependency characteristics who need to work in a hierarchical and organized milieu, community mental health centers tend to attract professionals who are rebellious, resentful of authority, and determined to go their own way. The result is a group likely to bring about innovation and new professional developments, but one that raises serious problems for statewide supervision and co-ordination.

The role-diffusion that has resulted from the entrance of psychiatric disciplines into the community has serious and far-reaching implications. It is particularly crucial at this point in the development of community mental health services, since training programs do not provide professional persons with a clear and unequivocal concept of the role of community practice.

Problems of closeness in the small community mental health center are particularly difficult to handle. Staff members live in the same social environment and often have, in addition to close working relationships, close social and interfamilial relationships. The relationship of the psychiatrist with other members of the community, the relationship of the staff to the governing board, and even the relationship of staff to patients are characterized by closeness, shifting role definition, and often by an anxiety-provoking intimacy that pierces professional armor.

Another problem for the community mental health worker is that of professional advancement. The psychiatrist who enters state hospital practice has before him a more or less predictable series of advancements leading eventually to superintendency of the state hospital. Where does a psychiatrist go who, immediately after residency, has become director of a community mental health center? The limits to which the community may develop a local service are in many instances fixed, and a clearly established ladder of advancement for the community psychiatrist has not as yet been elaborated.

Interagency problems also have serious implications. The relationship between community mental health centers and state hospitals will continue, for the foreseeable future, to be a threatening one for all those involved. In Kansas, the community mental health centers have consistently taken the lead in making overtures to state hospital personnel. Relationships between community mental health centers and professional training programs are also tenuous and fraught with conflict: the training centers often tend to believe that services are inferior in community centers, and community center personnel feel that the professionals in training centers are ignorant of the essential features of community mental health practice and are thus unfit to train others for community practice.

Basic conceptual problems will remain in the years ahead, despite our efforts to clarify some of them in this conference. The definition of the role of the community mental health practitioner demands our continuing attention.

Consultation and other preventive services must be systematically evaluated. We cannot continue to provide consultation on faith alone, since it clearly diverts scarce professional effort from clinical services. As Dr. Jack Downing of the San Mateo Mental Health Program once phrased it, "I'm afraid we're giving away all our samples and won't have anything left for the patients."

The question of administrative authority in community mental health programs will eventually have to be resolved more clearly.

Our position in Kansas is that the best qualified person in a program, no matter what his discipline, should be the director. However, this becomes increasingly unworkable in light of the unreliable judgment of the governing boards in determining who is best qualified for a directorship.

We should perhaps also consider whether we are overextending the egalitarian and democratic model. Is the community really ready for the mental health professional? By allowing professional people to work in communities, in centers governed by citizen governing boards, are we only exposing them to debasement and victimization?

We must face, as well, the question of whether we are deploying our professional resources in the best way. This question was considered at the 1964 annual meeting of the American Orthopsychiatric Association in a session entitled, "Are We Seeing the Right Patients?" Dr. Harry C. Bredemeier of the Urban Studies Center of Rutgers University made the point at that time (1) that if mental health services are essentially the same as services provided by a barber, in that the individual decides he needs a service and is willing to pay for it, then we are indeed seeing the right patients: those who are most motivated, most able to utilize treatment, and most able to pay for psychiatric, especially psychotherapeutic, services. But if community mental health services are to be part of the spectrum of socializing, civilizing, and social-control forces in our society, reliance on individual motivation and ability to pay is not sufficient.

How are we to blend our essentially individualistic, patient-centered, clinical orientation with a socially-oriented, conformity-stressing approach to community psychiatry?

Most important, we must have more and better epidemiological data about the incidence, prevalence, distribution, and types of mental and emotional disorders within our population. If rates of prevalence are as great as recent studies (8) have indicated, it may be necessary for us to reconsider our definition of the normal range of human emotional variability. We have tended to think that mental and emotional illness are like dental caries: extremely common but amenable to prevention and good treatment, so long as sufficient "psychic dentists" are available. This is perhaps a typically American illusion, rooted in our essential belief in the perfectibility of man. Our psychoanalytic experience should tell us that human perfectibility, as well as social perfectibility, are difficult if not impossible of achievement. And our heritage as biological scientists should remind us that the more complex a species, the greater the range of intraspecies variability. Perhaps a constant segment of our population will always display thought disorders, emotional lability, tenuous impulse control, and disabling anxiety.

But, for the present, we in Kansas are attempting to pursue a therapeutically optimistic, democratically-based, decentralized, and experimental course of development. We hope that our experience will broaden the body of substantive data concerning the translation of scientific knowledge about human disability into effective prevention, treatment, and rehabilitation.

References

1 BREDEMEIER, HARRY C. The clinics and their patients. Paper presented at the annual meeting of American Orthopsychiatric Association, Urban Studies Center, Rutgers University, New Brunswick, N.J., April, 1964.

2 CAPLAN, GERALD, ED. Prevention of Mental Disorders in Children. New York, Basic Books, 1961.

3 CAPLAN, GERALD. Principles of Preventive Psychology. New York, Basic Books, 1964.

4 DIVISION OF INSTITUTIONAL MANAGEMENT, DEPARTMENT OF SOCIAL WELFARE. Conservation of Human Resources, A Guide to the Community Mental Health Program in Kansas. Topeka, Kansas, 1964.

5 DIVISION OF INSTITUTIONAL MANAGEMENT, DEPARTMENT OF SOCIAL WELFARE. Standards for Community Mental Health Centers. Topeka, Kansas, 1964.

6 GOVERNMENTAL RESEARCH CENTER. Seminar for Directors of Mental Health Centers: A Report. Lawrence, Kansas, Univ. of Kansas, 1962.

7 JOINT COMMISSION ON MENTAL ILLNESS AND HEALTH. Action for Mental Health. New York, Basic Books, 1961.

8 LEIGHTON, DOROTHEA C., et al. The Character of Danger, Psychiatric Symptoms in Selected Communities, New York, Basic Books, 1963.

9 REVIEWS ON RESEARCH AND DATA ON DEVELOPMENT, No. 31. Washington, D.C., National Science Foundation, 1961.

Eight

Evaluating Community Care for Schizophrenic Patients in the United Kingdom

J. K. WING, M.D., PH.D., D.P.M.

I N TWO well-known articles first published in 1956, J. S. Bockoven traced the history of moral treatment in American psychiatry, from its heyday in the 1830's to its utter rejection by the turn of the century, through statistics given in the annual reports of the Worcester State Hospital in Massachusetts. Moral treatment implied a planned and socially integrated program of recreation, education, and occupation designed to "dispel the darkness and delusions that affect many" and "enable them to leave the institution not only rational, but better qualified by increased intelligence and power of self-control for encountering the troubles and performing the duties of life" (7). This combination of treatment by means of an intelligent attempt to alter the social influences to which the patient was exposed and a policy of early discharge back to the community anticipated by well over a century the essentials of what we are pleased to call our modern policies.

Whatever one thinks of the claims made for these methods at the time and of the statistics that were brought forward to support them, there is no doubt that when the era of moral treatment came to an end in the 1880's and 1890's, both in the United States and the United Kingdom, it was succeeded by a long custodial era from which we are only now re-emerging (39). In describing some of the problems associated with this further swing of the pendulum, which have become obvious in recent work in the United Kingdom, I may very well be putting forward propositions that also have relevance to the current situation in the United States. Our two countries may have more than historical trends in common. Nevertheless, I want to emphasize that my own material relates entirely to English hospitals, English systems of community care, English staff, and English patients. I have no close knowledge of American practices and policies and, if there are any parallels to be drawn, perhaps I could leave it to this well informed audience to draw them. I ought also to point out that most of the work I shall deal with has clear-cut imperfections of design, sampling, and methodology which rule out any possibility of dogmatic statement and allow only very tentative conclusions to be drawn.

CURRENT TRENDS IN THE UNITED KINGDOM

The most obvious measure of change in contemporary British psychiatry is the steady decline in the mental hospital population of England and Wales: it is not so marked in Scotland (18). The peak bed-occupancy of 33.5 per 10,000 population was reached in 1954 and there has since been a steady decline, which is still continuing (9). Something similar has been happening in the United States (8, 38). The Ministry of Health has projected this trend and foresees a time in the fairly near future when only eighteen beds per 10,000 will be needed (1, 65). Some British psychiatrists say that fewer still would suffice (61). If the number of beds can be at least halved and much of the remaining work transferred, as the English plan suggests, to psychiatric departments in general hospitals, then many of our large, old-fashioned, and remote mental hospitals could be closed altogether. The Minister of Health did perorate along these lines on one occasion, and a number of institutions actually were scheduled for closing.

However, the policy has come in for some sharp criticism (58, 64) which questioned the statistical basis for the Ministry's prediction, the adequacy of aftercare provisions, and the assumption that the decline in bed-occupancy was mainly due to early and successful treatment. In any case, we have as yet barely cleared away the overcrowding which used to be a feature of most mental hospitals. The trends certainly began in some areas well before they became noticeable nationally (there is still marked variation from place to place) and well before the tranquillizing drugs were introduced (45).

This important controversy is not yet over. Indeed, rather too much of the discussion about the future of our mental health services seems to be centered around it. Decisions made now may influence the shape of psychiatry for the next two generations, but, as is usual in decision-making, irrational elements are involved that threaten to swamp the rather small collection of relevant facts. At numerous symposia on the future of the mental hospital there seem to have been two camps, each with its quota of postures and attitudes, labels and slogans. On the "progressive" side we can include the therapeutic community (41), the open-door (3), the early discharge policy (65), rehabilitation (71), the day-hospital movement (22), community care (47), and family therapy (42). It is surprising that the drug firms remain so prosperous when there is such a welter of social nostrums and such energetic and able proponents. But in the other camp stand figures whose arguments are not to be lightly dismissed and who are not simply arguing for a return to the old days (40, 58, 64). Their slogans (the revolving door, the burden on the family, the schizophrenogenic mother, the prison replaces the hospital, does the community care?) represent real problems. How is one to evaluate it all?

BASIC STEPS IN EVALUATION

Mental health services have numerous interlocking functions and can be assessed at many different levels. The work I shall consider deals mainly with an issue which is fundamental from the point of view of the clinical psychiatrist: What effect do different patterns of service have on the symptoms and disabilities of individual patients, or the provocations and burdens of their relatives? If, using these criteria, one can find nothing to distinguish two apparently different mental health organizations, other levels of evaluation—technical, administrative, or economic —must be employed. On the other hand, all sorts of further investigations become indicated when a social factor of some kind emerges as a possible influence on symptoms. In an experimental study of very severely handicapped long-stay schizophrenic patients, Dr. Freudenberg and I found that improvement could be very rapidly effected on several indices of morbidity by getting a staff nurse to change from a passive to an active mode of supervision in a hospital workshop (74). When the passive conditions were restored, our measures reflected a rapid change back to the previous level of morbidity (cf. Group B, Trials 33–50, Figure 8.1).

Of course, simply to maintain a climate of opinion in which ward nurses are expected to exercise the mental functions of patients who are unable to spontaneously exercise them for themselves, and in which the nurses respond to this expectation, is quite a complicated matter. It would be different if one could rely on having ideal nurses—intelligent, quick to learn, persistent without supervision, well trained. We do have many like this, but we have many who are not. How can a hospital be organized so that nurses and attendants who are not ideal carry out the principles of care which will minimize a patient's symptoms or disabilities? Much of the force behind the idea of the therapeutic community lies in its promise that staff attitudes and behaviors can be influenced so that staff members will carry out what may be very simple therapeutic procedures. And a reason for scepticism about much that is claimed for therapeutic communities is that our knowledge of which social procedures will reduce which symptoms is still very scanty. There are a few good studies, but most investigators are content to describe very complex social organizations rather unsystematically and to rely on their own statement that the patients benefit in some way. Another very common and understandable error is the assumption that, because there have been administrative changes, the patients must be better. The principle I am enunciating denies this utterly. A decrease in the number of beds in a mental hospital, or in the proportion of readmissions, or an increase in the number of

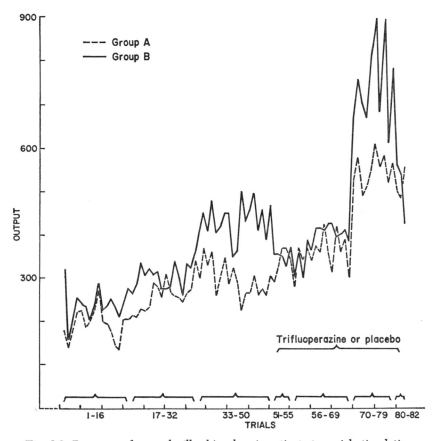

Fig. 8.1. Response of severely ill schizophrenic patients to social stimulation.

community care contacts after discharge, is not necessarily evidence that patients are better. This information may be useful, indeed essential, for many purposes, but it cannot be assumed that it tells us anything about morbidity.

Numerous recent studies (43, 56) have shown that community care and supervised drug administration can reduce the time that schizophrenic patients spend in the hospital. It is also, unfortunately, possible to reduce this time without making any extra aftercare provisions (75). Simply showing that the time in the hospital can be decreased tells one very little about the illness, the patients, or the patients' relatives.

Schizophrenia as a model for analysis. The advantage of this principle of evaluation is that it enables one to set up standards for judging whether or not services are successful. The disadvantage, from a research worker's point of view, is that standards are very difficult to define, and that they are different for different psychiatric conditions. What is suitable for mental subnormality will not be suitable for mania or, a fortiori, for mild affective disorders. I propose to select one group of conditions as a model for analysis, to show what might be done in investigation of services for the mentally ill.

Schizophrenia is a term that does not always mean the same thing on both sides of the Atlantic. I use it in its Kraepelinian sense to include only people who have had specific abnormal experiences which are elaborated as certain kinds of delusions and hallucinations, or who have shown specific abnormal behavior. I do not include simple schizophrenia, pseudoneurotic schizophrenia, latent schizophrenia, borderline schizophrenia, or schizoid or paranoid personality, unless the Kraepelinian symptomatology has clearly been present at some stage. Schizophrenia, thus defined, is still a heterogeneous collection of conditions, but it will serve as a useful model for my purpose.

In the first place, schizophrenia has always been regarded as a severe and crippling illness with a poor prognosis. In British mental hospitals, where about three-quarters of the patients have been resident for more than two years, two-thirds of this long-stay population are suffering from a form of schizophrenia. The chance that a first admitted patient with this diagnosis would be discharged within two years used to be less than even. After two years, his chance of being discharged at all during his lifetime declined rapidly (*11*). But for the accumulation of schizophrenic patients, we should hardly have a long-stay problem, and mental hospitals would be quite different places. Schizophrenics, by reason of their numbers and prolonged residence, acquired, transmitted, and partially determined the peculiar culture of the hospital community (*63*).

Schizophrenia is a useful condition to study for a second reason: today, fewer than 15 per cent of first admitted patients stay as long as two years (*10, 14*). The old long-stay schizophrenic population is not being replaced at anything like the previous rate, and this is one of the main reasons for the decline in mental hospital bed-occupancy. The situation in many parts of the United States is similar (21, 26, 37). There is also the advantage for a research worker that the process of selecting a series of schizophrenic patients for study by making a diagnosis on the basis of information in mental hospital case notes can be relatively reliable (54).

Chronic disabilities in schizophrenia. The handicaps of chronic schizophrenic patients have been studied in some detail and may be divided into two classes. The first group consists of the chronic symptoms of the illness which detract from the patient's capacity to work for his living or hinder his ability to play a full social role in the community. Much of the work on psychological deficit in schizophrenia has been concerned with two large symptom-clusters: mental slowness, inability to maintain a set, lack of attention or motivation, etc., which are variants of the clinical symptom of affective blunting; and a disturbance of associations, or over-inclusiveness. Recent work has confirmed that chronic schizophrenic patients are slow on psychomotor indices, slow to learn, and show a poor response to incentives (52, 53, 66). When a response can be demonstrated, there is a rapid relapse when the incentive is withdrawn (74).

In the ward, abnormal behavior can be measured by rating scales which yield indices of social withdrawal (including highly intercorrelated items such as slowness, underactivity, withdrawal, lack of leisure interests, poor care of appearance or cleanliness, and lack of conversation) and socially embarrassing behavior (70).

These chronic symptoms are very evident when schizophrenics are compared with physically disabled people in a mixed rehabilitation unit. The former are more frequently said by occupational supervisors to be slow, to lack initiative, and to have impaired capacity for independent judgment. They cannot make complicated decisions and they lack manual skill (68). Even the least handicapped patients from a good mental hospital showed marked social withdrawal at the industrial rehabilitation unit, though they were not unfriendly when approached.

The other large group of handicaps which hinder the resettle-

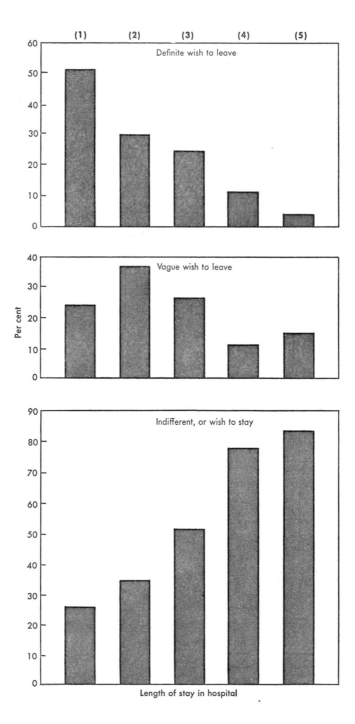

ment of chronic schizophrenic patients arises secondarily. The disabilities accumulate because the patients have been diagnosed as ill, but they are not actually part of the disease process. The most important examples are changes in self-attitudes and in personal habits brought about by institutionalism or unemployment or rejection by close relatives. Such changes can be at least as handicapping as the primary disabilities. Secondary handicaps always accumulate where there are severe primary disabilities; this has been demonstrated with physical abnormalities as well (30, 36). In schizophrenia, they are particularly easy to demonstrate (69). The longer a patient has been in the hospital, for example, the less likely is he to want to leave, or to have any realistic plans for a future life outside, as is illustrated in Figure 8.2.

This increasing dependence is part of a syndrome of institutionalism which represents a major problem in rehabilitation. Personal habits are also markedly affected, in proportion to the degree to which the hospital shows Goffman's characteristics of a total institution (28). If the patient does not practice traveling to work, clocking in on time, following workshop routines, conforming to group standards in dress and manners, acting the role of father or employee or shopper, new habits may develop which are maladaptive so far as outside society is concerned, and which preclude the possibility of resettlement.

Although the secondary disabilities, which form a large part of the syndrome of institutionalism, are the easiest ones to demonstrate, it seems very possible that something equivalent takes place in patients who do not remain for long periods in the hospital. In a survey of unemployed physically disabled men, Hewitt found that the only occupation all had in common was walking the streets and that there was a marked deterioration in

Fig. 8.2. Proportions of patients with various attitudes toward leaving the hospital in five length-of-stay groups (data from two hospitals combined). Length of present stay in hospital: Group (1), $0 - 1.11$; Group (2), $2 - 4.11$; Group (3),

$$n = 71 \qquad\qquad n = 41$$

$5 - 9.11$; Group (4), $10 - 19.11$; Group (5), $20 - 35$.

$$n = 55 \qquad\qquad n = 53 \qquad\qquad n = 36$$

self-respect and in personal habits (*36*). The early discharge policy may prevent one kind of handicap and promote another.

SOCIAL INFLUENCES ON SEVERITY OF HANDICAPS

The mental hospital is one component of the community services—though it is not always regarded in this light—and it is worthwhile to consider the evidence that social conditions there can actually affect the abilities and disabilities of schizophrenic patients. Threatening, violent, and destructive behavior is now rare in British mental hospitals, as are gross catatonic symptoms (*69*). In a recent study made in hospitals where the new drugs were being fully utilized, it was possible to examine the question of how far different social policies and different administrative organizations affected the primary and secondary handicaps of patients, crudely measured (*15, 73*). Three hospitals were chosen because they had rather different reputations for the care of long-stay schizophrenic patients—one hundred equivalent patients were randomly selected in each and a standard process of clinical and social measurement undertaken. Among the social indices were included a count of the patient's personal possessions; the attitude of ward nurses to various proposals about the patient—could she be allowed to have matches, could she go outside the hospital, could she have a bath unattended, etc.; a measure of the restrictiveness of ward regimes—for how long were how many ward doors locked, and numerous similar items; and a time-budget of the patient's activities on the previous day. Most of the social measurements could be related directly to the patients in the series and thereby could be compared directly with the assessment of mental state.

As an example of the social differences we found between the hospitals, Figure 8.3 shows the proportion of patients in the three series who owned selected items of clothing, toilet articles, ornaments, etc. Personal possession was defined to include items that had been supplied by the hospital so long as they were recognized or labeled as the patient's own.

It is fairly clear that far more long-stay patients in Hospital A owned personal possessions of all kinds than in Hospital C. Seventy-nine per cent owned a handbag, for example, compared

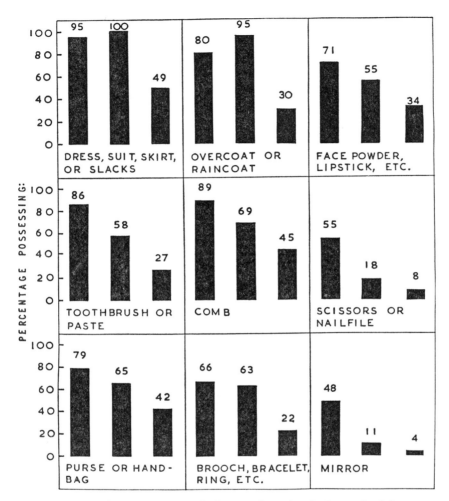

Fig. 8.3. Personal possessions, supplied privately or by the hospital, of long-stay female schizophrenic patients in three hospitals. In each cell, the blocks represent hospitals A, B, and C in that order.

with 42 per cent at Hospital C. A woman seems far less feminine without a handbag, and these apparently academic block diagrams contain facts which illustrate the processes of institutionalism. Conditions in Hospital B were intermediate between conditions in the other two. In rather obvious things, such as outer clothing, patients were as well off as those in Hospital A. In less obvious possessions, such as face powder or a toothbrush, they came about halfway between the other two groups. But they were not allowed to possess items that might have been harmful, such as scissors or a mirror, any more than patients in Hospital C. Hospital B, in fact, was in the process of improvement; it had made a start, but these telltale details showed that there was some way to go.

The other social indices told much the same story. The important thing, from our point of view, was that the social

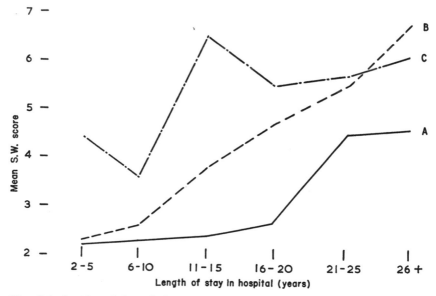

Fig. 8.4. Social withdrawal (S.W.) scores by length of stay in each of three hospitals (hospitals A, B, and C).

conditions under which the three series of patients were living were so demonstrably different that we were able to make a test of the hypothesis that the clinical state of the patients should vary accordingly. Figure 8.4 shows the social withdrawal scores (which represent ward behavior correlated with withdrawal, such as slowness, poor personal hygiene, lack of leisure interests, etc.).

The pattern of results is strikingly similar to that for personal possessions. Patients in Hospital A were markedly less withdrawn, whatever their length of stay, than patients in Hospital C, while those from Hospital B varied according to how long they had been in the hospital: long-stay patients were as withdrawn as if they had been in Hospital C, but relatively short-stay patients were as lively as those in Hospital A. Clinical state measured at a psychiatric interview confirmed these results. For example, the proportion of mute or almost mute patients in the three series, A, B, and C, was 6, 14, and 24 per cent, respectively.

Naturally, we considered several explanations for these results, but the hypothesis we were testing could not be excluded. A further test has been possible because the measurements were repeated at Hospital C recently, four years after the original study. Both social and clinical state have improved for the eighty-two patients out of the original hundred who are still alive and in the hospital. More than this, it is the patients whose social environment has most improved (particularly by a decrease in the time spent doing nothing) who are clinically better. The analysis shows no simple association with changes in drug treatment. We shall shortly be repeating the survey at the other two hospitals, and should then be in a position to accept or reject the original hypothesis more firmly and perhaps to elaborate others in detail and suggest what the mechanisms of improvement are. It seems clear, for example, that a change in personal appearance (because of a smarter hairdo, more attractive clothes, the application of make-up, etc.) can be brought about "mechanically" by dedicated nursing and a good hospital beauty parlor, without the patient's mental condition necessarily improving at all. On the other hand, increasing the activity of a hitherto inactive patient is much more likely to be associated with a decrease in social withdrawal and an increase in alertness and conversation. The former type of therapeutic activity is not wasted so long as it is associated with the latter. As the patient improves clinically, she can benefit, by a decrease in secondary handicaps, from her smarter appearance and begin to maintain it herself.

Rehabilitation of long-stay patients. Since the chronic symptoms and the secondary handicaps of long-stay schizophrenic patients appear to be influenced by the social conditions found in different mental hospitals, it is a reasonable assumption that the social conditions of the patient could be deliberately changed in order to bring about a reduction in handicaps and thus to maximize the chances of resettlement. British hospitals have progressed as far as most in this direction (25), but efforts at assessment have been infrequent.

Once rehabilitation is defined in terms of the disabilities, primary and secondary, which hinder the settlement of a patient in congenial work and prevent him from performing a full social role (71), a design for an evaluative study becomes fairly clear. In fact, it was possible to measure the disabilities of long-stay schizophrenic men, both severely and moderately ill, who either went to a special industrial rehabilitation unit or stayed behind in the mental hospital as controls (68). The severely ill patients, who had great difficulty in conducting a normal conversation and therefore would have been immediately obvious to an employer, did improve somewhat in rated symptomatology, but not in their attitudes to work—none of them was resettled. The moderately ill patients developed much more definite and realistic attitudes toward work and a good proportion were successfully resettled. The results of this study were confirmed and extended in a subsequent investigation using only moderately ill patients (72). A great deal of aftercare and supervisory work was done by psychiatrists, social workers, and employment officers, and places in sheltered factories were made available. Under these conditions, which are better than those generally available in the United Kingdom, about half the patients were working satisfactorily one year after being admitted to the project. The patients' disabilities did not disappear, though the secondary handicaps did show improvement. When one considers the excellent evidence now available (29) that individuals who later become schizophrenic may be handicapped long before they even see a psychiatrist, it is not surprising that the results of efforts at rehabilitation, perhaps twenty to thirty years later, are not one hundred per cent successful (5, 16).

The model for analysis of the problems involved in the rehabilitation of chronic schizophrenic patients which I have sketched here, and which may apply to other severe and chronically disabling psychiatric conditions, is based on the kind of

scheme which experts have long used for the physically handicapped (59). If patients have a continuing disability, one can
hope that it may spontaneously improve, and one can take all the
obvious steps to diminish it, but if it still remains, that is not the
end of the matter. Without giving up hope, one can provide social
circumstances in which the patient can live with dignity and
enjoyment of his residual faculties, in which the accumulation of
secondary handicaps is minimized, and in which the amount of
personal freedom and independence is as great as it can be. This
means creating a whole range of services which will provide a
ladder from the ward back into the community for the most
severely disabled patient. These services are certainly not generally available in the United Kingdom. However, there are working models of each part of the necessary services somewhere in
the country, and some day, no doubt, it will be possible to
assemble all the parts together and provide a comprehensive
service (25).

Short-stay patients. We turn now to a consideration of the
social problems of schizophrenic patients who are currently being
admitted to the hospital for the first time. Fewer than 15 per cent
of them stay in the hospital, on the first occasion, for as long as
two years. The median length of stay is about four months. We
want to know whether the shorter stay is accompanied by a
decrease in the chronicity of the disease. Institutionalism is
obviously avoided, but do other social disabilities develop instead? What is the patient's home like compared to a hospital
ward? How do the relatives make out as nurses? What burdens
do they carry? If the patient remains handicapped, are the
services which we have seen to be needed for long-stay patients
available outside the hospital?

Four members of our unit collaborated in a follow-up study of
schizophrenic men discharged from London mental hospitals in
1959 and 1960, in order to find some of the answers to these
questions (13, 51, 55, 75). I have emphasized that the changing
attitudes of long-stay patients are the central issue in institutionalism, as far as rehabilitation is concerned. The contrast with
short-stay patients is very marked. Out of over a hundred
patients, only one said he wished to stay in the hospital, two

appeared indifferent, and seven were not sure, but the rest (91 per cent) were definite in their wish to leave. About a quarter of the patients thought that their own present or past hallucinations indicated that they were, or had been, mentally ill. However, nearly half thought that equivalent symptoms in someone else would mean that he was mentally ill and 60 per cent thought that a casual observer would say that such a person was ill. The patients were confident about the future. Most of them thought that their relatives would welcome them or that they would easily find lodgings, and that getting work would be no problem.

At the time of leaving the hospital, 34 per cent of the patients were still actively deluded and only 27 per cent appeared completely free of symptoms. However, most patients had only mild symptoms. Forty per cent of relatives (usually the mother or wife was interviewed) said they would welcome the patient home, 25 per cent were accepting but not enthusiastic, 21 per cent were doubtful, and 13 per cent opposed. Unfavorable attitudes were often associated with a previous history of antisocial behavior. In the event, none actually refused to accept the patient.

Forty-three per cent of the patients were readmitted to hospital during the year after discharge, and a further 13 per cent deteriorated markedly in clinical condition although they were not readmitted. We categorized the eighty-four patients who were living at home according to the effect they had on their families. In 41 per cent of cases they were welcomed or tolerated: most of these patients had good work records and symptoms were not severe. In 14 per cent there was severe tension in the home: the atmosphere was strained and uncomfortable, with a pervading sense of unease about what the patient would do next. In the remaining 45 per cent the patient showed behavior which relatives found very distressing, either because he was threatening, violent, suicidal, or noisy at night, or because he involved his relatives in his delusions, openly accusing his wife, for example, of attempting to poison him. This period usually culminated in a social crisis, in which the patient's abnormal behavior could no longer be contained privately within the family but became visible in public. Some official would then be called in and the patient readmitted to the hospital.

I should emphasize that these results were obtained in a large city, part of an even larger conurbation, three to four years ago. The difficulties of providing good community services in such areas are well known. Patients did, in fact, make contact with their general practitioners (73 per cent of cases, 28 per cent regularly) and with outpatient clinics (58 per cent of cases, 21 per cent regularly). These visits, however, did not prevent crises. There was very little domiciliary visiting, except after a crisis had occurred. The vocational services were contacted quite frequently but mainly by the most handicapped patients, and the results were not very good.

In a subsequent study, members of the unit have studied the outcome, over five years, of schizophrenic patients admitted to three mental hospitals in 1956. None of the hospitals was in a conurbation, and the services available were more extensive, including a day hospital and routine domiciliary aftercare. There was very little difference between the three groups, and it is instructive to compare the progress of the first admitted patients with the outcome in two earlier series. Mayer-Gross (50) followed up, sixteen years later, patients with early schizophrenia admitted to the Heidelberg Clinic in 1912 and 1913. Harris, Norris, Linker, and Shepherd (35) followed, for five years, patients admitted to the Maudsley Hospital for insulin coma treatment from 1945 to 1948. The results are shown in Figure 8.5.

The proportions of patients in the three series who were alive, out of the hospital, working, and reasonably well mentally at the time of follow-up are 35, 45, and 55 per cent. The proportions who were out of the hospital, alive, but unwell or unemployed, are 3, 21, and 32 per cent. The proportions in hospitals or dead are 62, 34, and 13 per cent. These figures are not strictly comparable because of variations in excess mortality and numbers followed up, but they do give a rough basis for comparison.

A considerable improvement in prognosis can be claimed, though we should have to wait another eleven years to be sure, but part of it seems to have taken place before the new era had

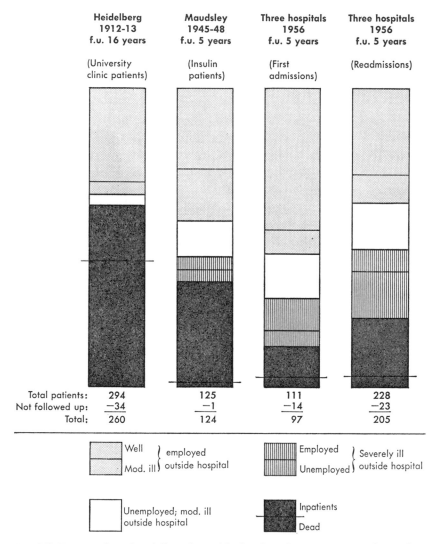

Fig. 8.5. Four studies that followed up (f.u.) schizophrenic patients admitted to hospitals in order to determine various social and clinical outcomes.

properly begun! Even among schizophrenic patients first admitted in 1956, over one quarter were in hospitals (and had been for at least six months) or were severely disturbed in the community five years later. Another 16 per cent were in the community and unable to work or maintain a home, although

their symptoms caused only moderate social disturbance. However, 55 per cent could be said to be "social recoveries," if one
includes a number whose adjustment was rather precarious. Of
patients who had been in the hospital before 1956 and were
readmitted in that year, only 38 per cent were working and
reasonably well in 1961.

The kinds of chronic symptoms shown by patients at the end of
the follow-up period were much the same as those seen in long-
stay patients. The secondary disabilities were different from those
of institutionalism but no less severe.

SOME SPECIFIC PROBLEMS OF COMMUNITY CARE

Before making some tentative suggestions about the sort of
community services which might possibly be able to cope with
the problems I have described, I should like to discuss briefly a
number of specific problems that have come up many times in our
studies and in those of other workers.

1. *Drug administration.* Pasamanick and his colleagues (56,
60) have provided preliminary evidence that chlorpromazine is
valuable in the community treatment of schizophrenic patients
and have emphasized the need for supervision to ensure that
patients follow the prescription.

In our London survey, 80 per cent of the patients were
prescribed drugs, most of which were major tranquilizers, at
some time during the follow-up year. Examination of the quantity
of drug issued and careful questioning of patients and relatives
made possible a decision, in nearly all cases, about whether the
drug had been taken as directed. Parkes (55) calculated that the
drug was taken as intended for only about half of the periods
during which it was prescribed. Usually a course of treatment
was terminated prematurely, for example, when a patient returned to work, or when the supply given him at the time of
discharge ran out. Some never took the drug at all.

A similar result was found in a Scottish survey (57), and it was
also clear, as it was in our material, that patients who did not take
drugs as advised had poorer outcomes. Whether this was because
relapsing patients gave up taking tablets or because stopping the
medication precipitated a deterioration in clinical state was not

altogether clear, although Pasamanick's work would to some extent support the latter hypothesis.

2. *Social crises.* Sixty-nine per cent of all 339 key admissions in our comparative survey followed a social emergency of some sort. The most common cause of admission was violent, threatening, or destructive behavior or a suicide attempt (36 per cent). Markedly odd behavior, excitement, noisiness, or other socially unacceptable behavior accounted for the other 33 per cent. Readmissions during the follow-up period followed a similar pattern.

We were able to check, in one area, the approximate number of social crises which were not followed by admission to the hospital but were reported to the appropriate community workers. Just over half the patients were involved in social crises—that is, harmful or acting out behavior which led to emergency action; in one-half of these cases the patient was not admitted.

The problems that families encountered through having an unrecovered patient at home were highlighted by these crises, which seem to be the central problem for community care. None of the services we have investigated has been able to prevent them. Smith, Pumphrey, and Hall (62) came to very similar conclusions about a series of one hundred admissions for schizophrenia in 1961–62.

3. *Work.* The handicaps of many of the patients made it very difficult for them to obtain or hold down a job successfully. There is a national organization of services, available free to any registered disabled person, which includes rehabilitation units, vocational guidance, special help in placement, and sheltered factories for those who cannot work in open industry. However, unless the hierarchy of officials who staff this service can be brought into more intimate contact with mental health personnel, and unless places in sheltered workshops can be made available on a large scale, schizophrenic patients in the community will continue to show a high unemployment rate. There is still a great deal of prejudice to be overcome, but it is also fair to point out that patients with fluctuating symptoms are often referred to employment exchanges or rehabilitation units as a last resort, because the doctor or social worker cannot think what else to do.

4. *Family problems.* Relatives were usually unable to suggest in any detail what alternative services might have been helpful to them or to the patient, but a number of very common problems did emerge. They described effects on their own or their children's health, restrictions on leisure or other activities, and financial difficulties. Twenty-three per cent of informants where there was a child in the house at the time said that the patient was having an adverse effect. The problems they described—enuresis, delinquency, neurotic symptoms, psychosomatic illness—might not have been due to the patient at all, but the relatives thought they were.

Nevertheless, most relatives were quite sure that they did not want the patient to stay in the hospital for a long period. The exceptions usually concerned very severely handicapped patients.

5. *Family relationships.* In an earlier study (12), Brown and Carstairs found that the prognosis of discharged long-stay schizophrenic men varied according to whether they returned to live with mother, wife, sibling, or landlady. In the London survey, we investigated this curious finding in more detail (13). Ratings of the emotional involvement of a key relative (usually wife or mother) with the patient, made a week or two after discharge during a joint interview at home, were significantly associated with outcome a year later. Figure 8.6 shows that a much larger proportion of patients whose relatives had a high involvement with them deteriorated clinically or were readmitted than patients in the low involvement group. Moreover, the patients who spent the most time with their relatives were the most likely to get worse.

This association could be explained in a number of ways: for example, that patients with the poorest prognosis had previously shown behavior which would lead to an intense emotional reaction in their relatives. Previous history and severity of condition at the time of discharge were indeed related to outcome, but the relationship with the relative provided an independent and significant component to the prediction. Much work has been done on the family relationships of schizophrenic patients, more of it in the United States (2, 46, 76) than in the United Kingdom

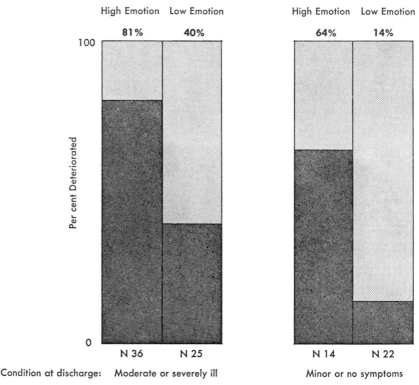

Fig. 8.6. Clinical deterioration of ninety-seven schizophrenic patients during year after discharge, by emotional involvement of key relative. (The number of patients reported on per column is given at the foot of the column.)

(*44*). We are impressed with the complications involved in collecting useful data in this field and consider that theory has outrun fact by too large a margin. However, the problems, though difficult, do seem susceptible to ordinary methods of scientific investigation.

6. *Social work in the community.* Our main impression in all our follow-up studies was that the number of workers available to deal with a large number of patients was very small. The problem of numbers is formidable. Assuming that there are two hundred schizophrenic patients needing help in an area of 100,000 people, and that one visit a month is sufficient for good care and supervision, five social workers could easily be kept busy doing nothing else but looking after these patients, attending the relevant case conferences, etc. Most local authority areas in the

United Kingdom only have about five social workers (often un-trained) for all mental health purposes, including the care of the mentally subnormal, in an area of 100,000 people.

The task of the social worker is to gather information for herself and other members of the team, to obtain the trust of patient and relatives (itself often an impossible task), to give advice on the services available to patient and family (which will only be helpful if the relationship of trust has been built up so that the advice is accepted and if the services are actually available), and to counsel the relatives on the proper management of the patient. The latter function may well be shared with the psychiatric health visitor. These tasks need skill, judgment, and, above all, time. Our impression, in the areas we studied, was that social workers were very rarely working under conditions that were anything like optimum for good work, and even in areas where routine as well as emergency visits were being made, there was little evidence of any preventive effect.

SERVICES OF THE FUTURE

Mental health services should be planned to alleviate or contain the social problems caused by psychiatric illnesses. They must therefore be grounded in facts.

For schizophrenia, the facts are that about 40 per cent of first admitted patients in 1956 were still severely handicapped five years later, including those unable to work or run a home. The most common handicaps were slowness and other disabilities correlated with social withdrawal (70), inability to undertake work involving decision-making or responsibility, and difficulty with personal relationships. The condition of many of the chroni-cally ill patients fluctuated considerably: emergencies could occur at any time, perhaps at night or on weekends. The patient was not necessarily co-operative. He did not always take his tablets, keep his appointments, stick at his job, or agree to enter the hospital when advised. His relationships with his family were sometimes strained and difficult to an extent which many of us would find intolerable. The patient's relatives did not, in return, always provide the most therapeutic environment for him to recover in.

It might be objected that these facts only hold in areas where a really effective service has not been provided. In that case I have yet to see a really effective service, but it is true that a number of separate components exist which, if they could be brought together, might provide an ideal organization.

We can learn many lessons from the study of long-stay patients and the ways in which their social environment has been successfully modified in order to minimize their symptoms and disabilities and maximize their chances of resettlement. Short-stay patients are liable to be handicapped in very similar ways, and they may benefit from similar services. All the functions of the mental hospital (17) still need to be carried out. The day hospital, the night hospital, the week-end hospital, the observation ward, the short-stay and predischarge units, and the hostel are all fragments which can be separated from each other geographically as long as there is uniformity of direction and continuity of care. These lower rungs on the ladder of domestic resettlement need to be supplemented higher up by family care, supervised lodgings, and houses in the community which have been taken over for the use of ex-patients (20, 49). The other ladder, that of industrial resettlement (5, 6, 19)—from planned occupational therapy through various forms of sheltered work to rehabilitation workshops and finally resettlement units in ordinary factories—is easier to provide. The widest range of services is provided in Bristol, England (19), but very few areas can claim anything like this coverage.

As well as these two fundamental types of agency, supporting services are required—emergency clinic, outpatient department, domiciliary social work and nursing service, social club, employment exchange—and the staff to run them. Unless these services are of high quality, patients and their relatives will not use them.

The major problem, once these facilities have been provided, is co-ordinating their use so that the progress of the patient from one agency to another involves no time-lags and no sudden jumps from one level to another. This can best be ensured if a list is maintained of all the patients who are at risk in a given area and a team of experts keeps track of the latest situation of every person on the list.

It seems likely that several different patterns of care could be made to work. The place of the small, open mental hospital at the center of its catchment area, in close association with a general hospital, with staff working in the community as well as in the words, should not be underestimated. However, from the point of view of a research worker and of the administrator who wants efficient services, the obvious thing to do is to set up different models in different parts of the country, with independent evaluation procedures built in. Much is already known about the appropriate methodology (27, 31, 52, 33, 34).

Research workers in this field are agreed that the more detailed, systematic, and controlled the investigation of social and medical services, the less likelihood there is of positive results. Foulds (23) says the same of drug studies. To accept this is pure gain. If we know what really happens now, we have a guide to future action and a standard by which to judge whether the action has been successful. In fact, we have the basis for successful planning.

To put these findings in perspective, a final point should be remembered. I have chosen schizophrenia as a model for analysis because the social problems associated with it are among the most difficult in psychiatry. Schizophrenia is an acid test for the mental health services, but it is only a part of what they have to deal with. The picture is much brighter, particularly in certain areas in Britain (24, 48, 49, 67), when services as a whole are examined. Relatively speaking, our mental health organization is hard to beat. The combination of early discharge and detailed aftercare for those who need it seems to be the accepted pattern. There are gaps and blind spots, but none of them need be insuperable.

References

1 A HOSPITAL PLAN FOR ENGLAND AND WALES. Cmd. No. 1604, London, H.M.S.O., 1962.
2 BATESON, G., JACKSON, D. D., HALEY, J., AND WEAKLAND, J. Towards a theory of schizophrenia. *Behav. Sci.* 1:251, 1956.
3 BELL, G. M. A mental hospital with open doors. *Int. J. soc. Psychiat.* 1:42, 1955.

4   BELLAK, L., AND BLACK, B. B. The rehabilitation of psychotics in the community. *Amer. J. Orthopsychiat. 30*:346, 1960.

5   BENNETT, D. H., FOLKARD, S., AND NICHOLSON, A. K. Resettlement unit in a mental hospital. *Lancet 2*:539, 1961.

6   BENNETT, D. H., AND WING, J. K. "Sheltered Workshops for the Psychiatrically Handicapped." In *Trends in the Mental Health Services,* edited by H. Freeman and J. Farndale. New York, Pergamon, 1963.

7   BOCKOVEN, J. S. *Moral Treatment in American Psychiatry.* New York, Springer, 1963.

8   BRILL, H., AND PATTON, R. E. Clinical-statistical analysis of population changes in New York State mental hospitals since introduction of psychotropic drugs. *Amer. J. Psychiat. 119*:20, 1962.

9   BROOKE, EILEEN. Factors affecting the demand for psychiatric beds. *Lancet 2*:1211, 1962.

10 BROOKE, EILEEN. *A Cohort Study of Patients First Admitted to Mental Hospitals in 1954 and 1955.* London, H.M.S.O., 1963.

11 BROWN, G. W. Length of hospital stay and schizophrenia. *Acta Psychiat. Scand. 35*:414, 1960.

12 BROWN, G. W., CARSTAIRS, G. M., AND TOPPING, G. G. Post-hospital adjustment of chronic mental patients. *Lancet 2*:685, 1958.

13 BROWN, G. W., MONCK, E. M., CARSTAIRS, G. M., AND WING, J. K. The influence of family life on the course of schizophrenic illness. *Brit. J. prev. soc. Med. 16*:55, 1962.

14 BROWN, G. W., PARKES, C. M., AND WING, J. K. Admissions and readmissions to three London mental hospitals. *J. ment. Sci. 107*:1070, 1961.

15 BROWN, G. W., AND WING, J. K. A comparative clinical and social survey of three mental hospitals. *Sociol. Rev. Monogr. 5*: 1962.

16 CATTERSON, A. G., BENNETT, D. H., AND FREUDENBERG, R. K. A survey of longstay schizophrenic patients. *Brit. J. Psychiat. 109*:750, 1963.

17 CLARK, D. Administrative psychiatry 1942–1962. *Brit. J. Psychiat. 109*:178, 1963.

18 DEPARTMENT OF HEALTH FOR SCOTLAND. *Hospital Plan for Scotland.* Cmd. No. 1602, London, H.M.S.O., 1962.

19 EARLY, D. The Industrial Therapy Organisation (Bristol): The first two years. *Lancet 1*:435, 1963.

20 EARLY, D. "Domestic Resettlement." In *Psychiatric Hospital Care,* edited by H. Freeman. London, Balliere, Tindall, and Cassell, 1965.

21 EPSTEIN, L., AND MORGAN, R. Trends in release rates of schizophrenic patients. *Comprehen. Psychiat. 2*:196, 1961.

22 FARNDALE, J. *The Day Hospital Movement in Great Britain.* London, Pergamon, 1961.

23 FOULDS, G. A. Clinical research in psychiatry. *J. ment. Sci. 104*:259, 1958.

24 FREEMAN, H. "Local Authority Services." In *Trends in the Mental*

Hospital Services, edited by H. Freeman and J. Farndale. New York, Pergamon, 163.

25 FREEMAN, H., ED. *Psychiatric Hospital Care.* London, Balliere, Tindall, and Cassell, 1965.

26 FREYHAN, F. A. Course and outcome of schizophrenia. *Amer. J. Psychiat. 112*:161, 1955.

27 GARDNER, E., MILES, H. C., BAHN, ANITA, AND ROMANO, J. All psychiatric experience in a community. *Arch. gen. Psychiat.* 9:369, 1963.

28 GOFFMAN, E. "The Characteristics of Total Institutions." In *Asylums,* by E. Goffman. New York, Doubleday, 1961.

29 GOLDBERG, E. M., AND MORRISON, S. Schizophrenia and social class. *Brit. J. Psychiat. 109*:785, 1963.

30 GOODMAN, N., RICHARDSON, S. A., DORNBUSCH, S. M., AND HASTORF, A. H. Variant reactions to physical disabilities. *Amer. sociol. Rev.* 28:429, 1963.

31 GORWITZ, K., BAHN, ANITA, CHANDLER, CAROLINE, AND MARTIN, W. A. Planned uses of a statewide psychiatric register for aiding mental health in the community. *Amer. J. Orthopsychiat.* 33:494, 1963.

32 GRAD, JACQUELINE, AND SAINSBURY, P. Mental illness and the family. *Lancet 1*:544, 1963.

33 GRANT, J. D. It's time to start counting. *Crime and Delinquency,* July, 1962, p. 259.

34 GRUENBERG, E. M., KASIUS, R. V., AND HUXLEY, M. Objective appraisal in a group of longstay hospital patients. Paper presented at the Third World Congress of Psychiatry, Montreal, June, 1961.

35 HARRIS, A., NORRIS, VERA, LINKER, I., AND SHEPHERD, M. Schizophrenia: A prognostic and social study. *Brit. J. prev. soc. Med. 10*:106, 1956.

36 HEWITT, M. The unemployed disabled man. *Lancet 2*:523, 1949.

37 ISRAEL, R. H., AND JOHNSON, N. A. Discharge and readmission rates in 4254 consecutive first admissions of schizophrenia. *Amer. J. Psychiat. 112*:903, 1956.

38 JOINT INFORMATION SERVICE. *Fifteen Indices.* Washington, D.C., American Psychiatric Association and National Association for Mental Health, 1964.

39 JONES, KATHLEEN. *Mental Health and Social Policy 1845–1959.* London, Routledge & Kegan Paul, 1960.

40 JONES, KATHLEEN, AND SIDEBOTHAM, R. *Mental Hospitals at Work.* London, Routledge & Kegan Paul, 1962.

41 JONES, MAXWELL. *Social Psychiatry: In the Community, in Hospitals and in Prisons.* Springfield, Thomas, 1962.

42 KAHN, J. H. "Community Responsibilities for Mental Health." In *Trends in the Mental Health Services,* edited by H. Freeman and J. Farndale. New York, Pergamon, 1963.

43 KRIS, ELSE. Five years' experience with the use of drugs and

psychotherapy in a community aftercare clinic. *Amer. J. Pub. Health.* 52:9, 1962.

44 LAING, R. D., AND ESTERSON, A. *Sanity, Madness and the Family: I. Families of Schizophrenics.* London, Tavistock, 1964.

45 LEWIS, A. J. "The Impact of Psychotropic Drugs on the Structure, Function and Future of Psychiatric Services (a) In the Hospitals." *Neuropsychopharmacology,* Vol. I, *Proceedings of the First International Congress of Neuropsychopharmacology, Rome, 1958,* edited by P. B. Bradley, P. Deniker, and C. Raduoco-Thomas. Amsterdam, Elsewier, 1959, pp. 207–12.

46 LIDZ, T., AND FLECK, S. "Schizophrenia, Human Integration, and the Role of Family." In *The Etiology of Schizophrenia,* edited by D. D. Jackson. New York, Basic Books, 1960.

47 MACMILLAN, D. Community treatment of mental illness. *Lancet* 2:201, 1958.

48 MACMILLAN, D. "Hospital-community Relationships." In *An Approach to the Prevention of Disability from Chronic Psychoses.* New York, Milbank Memorial Fund, 1958.

49 MAY, A. R., JONES, D. M. H., AND BRUGGEN, P. Restoring the psychiatrically disabled to the community. *Lancet* 2:241, 1963.

50 MAYER-GROSS, W. "Die Klinik." In *Handbuch der Geisteskrankheiten,* Vol. IX, edited by O. Bumke. Berlin, Springer, 1932, p. 534.

51 MONCK, ELIZABETH M. Employment experiences of 127 discharged schizophrenic men in London. *Brit. J. prev. soc. Med.* 17:101–10, 1963.

52 O'CONNOR, N., HERON, A., AND CARSTAIRS, G. M. Work performance of chronic schizophrenics. *Occup. Psychol.* 30:153, 1956.

53 O'CONNOR, N., AND RAWNSLEY, K. Incentives with paranoid and non-paranoid schizophrenics in a workshop. *Brit. J. med. Psychol.* 32:133, 1959.

54 PARKES, C. M. Inter-hospital and intra-hospital variations in the diagnosis and severity of schizophrenia. *Brit. J. prev. soc. Med.* 17:85, 1963.

55 PARKES, C. M., BROWN, G. W., AND MONCK, ELIZABETH M. The general practitioner and the schizophrenic patient. *Brit. med. J.* 1:972, 1962.

56 PASAMANICK, B., SCARPITTI, F. R., LEFTON, M., DINITZ, S., WERNERT, J. J., AND McPHEETERS, H. Home versus hospital care for schizophrenics. *J. Amer. Med. Ass.* 187:177, 1964.

57 REHIN, G. F., AND MARTIN, F. M. *Psychiatric Services in 1975.* London, P.E.P., 1963.

58 RENTON, C. A., AFFLECK, J. W., CARSTAIRS, G. M., AND FOREST, A. D. A follow-up study of schizophrenic patients in Edinburgh. *Acta Psychiat. Scand.* 39:548, 1963.

59 RUSK, H. A. *Rehabilitation Medicine.* London, Henry Kimpton, 1958.

60 SCARPITTI, F. R., LEFTON, M., DINITZ, S., AND PASAMANICK, B. Problems in a home care study for schizophrenics. *Arch. gen. Psychiat.* 10:143, 1964.

61 SILVERMAN, M. A comprehensive department of psychological medicine. *Brit. med. J.* 2:698, 1961.

62 SMITH, KATHLEEN, PUMPHREY, MURIEL, AND HALL, J. C. The "last straw": The decisive incident resulting in the request for hospitalization in 100 schizophrenic patients. *Amer. J. Psychiat.* 120:228, 1963.

63 SOMMER, R. Patients who grow old in a mental hospital. *Geriatrics* 14:581, 1959.

64 TITMUSS, R. M. "Community Care—Fact or Fiction?" In *Trends in the Mental Health Services,* edited by H. Freeman and J. Farndale. New York, Pergamon, 1963.

65 TOOTH, G. C., AND BROOKE, EILEEN. Trends in the mental hospital population and their effect on future planning. *Lancet* 1:710, 1961.

66 VENABLES, P. H. Stimulus complexity as a determinant of the reaction time of schizophrenics. *Canad. J. Psychol.* 12:187, 1958.

67 WEEKS, K. "The Plymouth Nuffield Clinic—A Community Mental Health Centre." In *Psychiatric Hospital Care,* edited by H. Freeman. London, Balliere, Tindall, and Cassell, 1965.

68 WING, J. K. A pilot experiment on the rehabilitation of long-hospitalised male schizophrenic patients. *Brit. J. prev. soc. Med.* 14:173–80, 1960.

69 WING, J. K. Institutionalism in mental hospitals. *Brit. J. soc. clin. Psychol.* 1:38–51, 1962.

70 WING, J. K. A simple and reliable subclassification of chronic schizophrenia. *J. ment. Sci.* 107:862–75, 1961.

71 WING, J. K. Rehabilitation of psychiatric patients. *Brit. J. Psychiat.* 109:635, 1963.

72 WING, J. K., BENNETT, D. H., AND DENHAM, J. *The Industrial Rehabilitation of Longstay Schizophrenic Patients.* Medical Research Council Memorandum No. 42, London, H.M.S.O. To be published.

73 WING, J. K., AND BROWN, G. W. Social treatment of chronic schizophrenia: A comparative survey of three mental hospitals. *J ment. Sci.* 107:847, 1961.

74 WING, J. K., AND FREUDENBERG, R. K. The response of severely ill chronic schizophrenic patients to social stimulation. *Amer. J. Psychiat.* 118:311, 1961.

75 WING, J. K., MONCK, E. M., BROWN, G. W., AND CARSTAIRS, G. M. Morbidity in the community of schizophrenic patients discharged from London mental hospitals in 1959. *Brit. J. Psychiat.* 110:10, 1964.

76 WYNNE, L., RYCKOFF, I., DAY, J., AND HIRSCH, S. Pseudo-mutuality in the family relations of schizophrenics. *Psychiatry* 21:205, 1958.

III

COMMUNITY PSYCHIATRY IN PERSPECTIVE

Nine

Planning and Practice Perspectives on the Boundaries of Community Psychiatry

ALFRED J. KAHN, D.S.W.

NOTHING dramatizes the significance of our question concerning the boundaries of community psychiatry more than current experience with the creation and operation of community mental health centers. Delinquents, unmarried mothers, school drop-outs, autistic children, unhappy adults, narcotics addicts, ambulatory schizophrenics, and many others have become the deliberate targets of mental health programs or of their own volition have crowded the newly-opened doors (1). Since clinicians, particularly psychiatrists, are the key helpers in the mental health center, it is the primary helping agency for all these people; and since its service is community-based in the sense that it is outside of a hospital and is not private practice, it is defined as community mental health. What the clinician does in the center is then defined as community psychiatry. All of this seems clear and natural. Why, then, should we be concerned with boundaries in any field, and in this one in particular?

WHY CONSIDER BOUNDARIES?

Some children's courts believe that they provide the central service for delinquents, drop-outs, and unmarried mothers. Some mental health centers consider these to be their clientele. Certain specialized agencies believe that they provide the primary aid for unmarried mothers, while youth counseling and employment programs make a major bid for drop-outs, for "potential" or "reformed" delinquents, and occasionally even for unmarried mothers. Furthermore, on those occasions when employment, court, or unmarried mothers' agencies do want a mental health center to take over one of their cases, their concept of the case may not coincide with that of the center.

All of this sounds like a problem of jurisdiction, to be resolved by mediation procedures, arbitration, and court decisions. In the world of competitive funding, intraprofessional power rivalry, and political involvement in social welfare, this is precisely what may be necessary. If the matter is pursued, however, it will be discovered that there are substantive issues involved that may permit rational processes to enter into the resolution of the question, whatever the format. For the boundaries issue both reflects and creates problems, and the way in which it is handled makes a substantial difference to those we would help.

Consider, for example, an intrafamilial problem whose overt manifestations take the form of parent-child difficulties, parent-parent conflict, and personality and school learning difficulties in the child. Place this problem in the rare community that has a professionally staffed program including a child guidance clinic, a school social work program, a family service agency, a child welfare service, and an adult mental health clinic. Make a random or an arbitrary decision as to referral. Observe the family outcome and the outcomes in comparable cases referred in the same fashion to other agencies in the community. It is clear that, even if the agency initially chosen subsequently confers with other agencies, the nature of the agency initially utilized makes a considerable difference in what occurs—psychiatric treatment, child placement, or school adjustment, for example—and that these differences affect the long-term status of the parents and children involved.

The choosing of an agency, which I call the problem of channeling, is not a matter of coin-tossing, although it may seem to some to be just that irrational (4). I have documented elsewhere a considerable body of evidence to the effect that social welfare channeling is influenced by a wide range of factors, only a few of which can in any sense be considered rooted in systematic concern for the people involved (8). These factors include the potential client's ethnic, religious, racial, social-class, or educational background; the professional or "field" identifications and related built-in biases of those who do the first-level screening; the adequacy of community information and referral resources; the availability of experimental programs and their definitions of their targets; the potential client's conception of the problem and his view of whether he should have, and take, a certain type of extrafamilial help; and agency resources, manpower policies, research interests, and competence.

Among the readily observable results of channeling determined by these variables are high rates of intake rejection, large numbers of case drop-outs after the initiation of a treatment plan, and a significant number of case failures labeled as "unmotivated" or "unable to use the service." The result is, in short, human suffering and wastage of resources (10).

This problem should be attacked on two fronts. First, channeling to social welfare services should be freed from professional and agency chauvinism and based instead on a rational community service strategy. The goal of this approach might be to create a system that does not demand that a potential patient either find a friend in the political power structure or be a fully educated person, sophisticated in the ways and functions of agencies. Solutions must be found at the level of the individual agency as well as on the community level, in the creation of a number of "open doors," as I have suggested elsewhere (9).

The second task is to define the role of each agency and service so that it is clear and understandable to those who are part of the channeling machinery and so that the agency can make optimal use of the knowledge and skills represented within it. To put it in the language or our discussion, the task is to define the boundaries of any given source of service—court, clinic, school, or treatment institution—so that the source becomes a definite entity, known and, in some sense, coherent from the point of view of patients, community referral channels, and agents as well as its own staff. A prerequisite to such coherence is a formulation of mission that translates staff, knowledge, and competence into a focused intervention system.

The term "intervention system" may be used generically to describe a segment of the social welfare structure (excluding the family or private enterprise) that plays a role in improving or maintaining people's incomes, health, or social functioning. Intervention systems—for example public assistance, corrections, and child welfare—generally coincide with social institutions or large organizations. The boundaries question, from a planning perspective, is one of defining the divisions between intervention systems at a given moment so as to optimize the use of knowledge and competence and to maximize the ability of potential users to draw upon the service. Tasks must then be subdivided among agencies and services within the system, and provisions made for case integration.

Should community psychiatry be considered an intervention system in this sense? If so, what are its boundaries? If community psychiatry is the system, what is community mental health? What is the relationship of all this to social psychiatry?

If the intervention system is community psychiatry, what is its distinguishing core? How should people be enabled to distinguish between community psychiatry and its peripheral, supportive, and housekeeping functions, the noise and static that often obscure the essence of a social institution?

SOCIAL PSYCHIATRY AND COMMUNITY PSYCHIATRY

There is some semantic confusion over the term "social psychiatry." Some of the professional literature tends to leave social psychiatry's boundaries with community psychiatry uncertain, stressing only their common ground. Goldston (6) assembled a series of efforts at definition that demonstrate this imprecision and overlapping, natural in an evolving field; but a number of authorities have begun to converge in their statements of the distinction between the two. Redlich and Pepper (6) see social psychiatry as "the study of psychiatric disorders and psychiatric therapy, hopefully including prevention, within a social setting. This implies that social psychiatry is defined as an exploration of social systems and culture and their impact on psychiatric phenomena rather than as a type of psychiatric practice." Jones (6) states, "In its widest sense the term implies the social factors associated with the living experiences of psychiatric patients or potential patients, whether in hospital or in the outside world." The Langley Porter staff (6) believe social psychiatry to be: "That part of psychiatry concerned with various aspects of society as it relates to emotional disturbance. Insofar as it is similar to social psychology, its emphasis is probably more theoretical than practical."

In the vocabulary of the present discussion, social psychiatry is not an intervention system. It is a field of theory and an area of research, and it exists at the point where psychiatric theory and social science converge. The term "community psychiatry," on the other hand, clearly implies a service or practice role. Investigation reveals, however, that whereas some consider community psychiatry itself to be an intervention system, others consider it to be merely a professional discipline within an intervention system they designate as "community mental health." Sometimes the specific usage grows out of imprecise language, but at other times it reflects a conviction that community psychiatry finds its characteristic outlet through an institutional base with broad preventive orientations, and that community psychiatry has no existence apart from such a base. It will be recalled that the illustration with which this paper began referred to what occurs in community mental health centers—in contrast to hospitals—as community mental health, and to what the physician does in such centers as community psychiatry.

If we accept this distinction as valid, then the question of the boundaries of community psychiatry becomes largely a problem to be solved within the medical profession and its subspecialty of psychiatry. As an internal problem of the psychiatric discipline, the definition of community psychiatry could not be wholly within the competence of an interdisciplinary conference; it should be dealt with in the way that medicine generally copes with problems of specialization.

We are thus faced with a choice. Shall we discuss an intervention system, to be called "community mental health," which, like all intervention systems in modern social welfare, involves many professions, subprofessions, and technical disciplines? Or shall we face the possibility that the intervention system is actually community psychiatry, and that it is more than a medical subspecialty, that it possesses all the characteristics of a complete system?

SERVICE BOUNDARIES

The effort to define community psychiatry generally begins with differentiations between it and traditional clinical psychiatry. The practitioner of the latter specialty, we are reminded, is oriented essentially toward the individual patient. The arena of his activity may be the office, clinic, or hospital, but he characteristically operates through a personal relationship with his patients (3, 2). If one were to begin a new system of nomenclature, the term "case psychiatry" would most accurately describe this procedure, since every psychiatrist takes clinical knowledge as his point of departure.

"Community psychiatry" is the term most often used to describe the psychiatrist's other roles. The community psychiatrist is described, for example, by Duhl as the one "concerned with optimizing the adoptive potential and psychosocial life skills, as well as lessening the amount of pathology, in population groups (communities, functional groups, etc.) by population-wide programs of prevention, case finding, care, treatment, and rehabilitation. The individual becomes important not only as an individual problem but also as a flag of a more general psychiatric need of a population group" (6).

The Langley Porter staff, who go even farther in stressing prevention and viewing treatment in this context, describe community psychiatry as "that subspecialty of psychiatry which directs its attention and efforts to community mental health problems. Its tools are consultation, in-service training, general public education; its targets, key groups and individuals in the community whose behavior and attitudes have broad influence over the lives of others; its goals, to reduce significantly the number of seriously disturbed individuals and to decrease the extent of malfunctioning of a significant number of those people designated as emotionally disturbed" (6).

In terms of some of these definitions, the practitioner of community psychiatry may also be a social worker, a psychologist, a nurse, or a member of a related profession who has had a degree of clinical training and has been prepared for the role. The validity of this notion depends, of course, on whether community psychiatry is considered a medical specialty or an over-all intervention system.

The problem of boundaries becomes apparent as one pursues the definition further. Caplan, for example, states, "Community psychiatry is based upon the acceptance by psychiatrists of responsibility for dealing with all the mentally disordered within the confines of a community. This responsibility focuses upon current cases, but also spreads to potential cases through programs of primary prevention" (2).

We must first consider the term "mentally disordered," which implies more than psychiatric illness: it apparently extends to those who are maladjusted in work, play, and school, as well as at home. Are any areas of difficulty in role enactment or social living omitted? The phrase "potential cases," when coupled with the category "mentally disordered," would seem to include all members of society, born and unborn. The reference to community would seem to exclude only hospitalized patients not on aftercare status. If one adds to this the related idea, widely stated, that the community psychiatrist must evolve new methods, one is describing a field that potentially involves all people, in all possible institutional contexts, as well as the social engineering and policy aspects of the institutions themselves. It should be recalled that the somewhat expansive definitions I have quoted do include these.

To follow this path is to include within community psychiatry almost all efforts to improve social life and affect social problems, as well as psychiatric treatment given outside private practice— and probably some of that, too. Is this expansive definition useful, or would a more modest delimitation facilitate the organization of psychiatric services and the over-all task of community planning? Is it, in fact, possible to cope with the boundaries problem by reference to types of problems or goals—the larger components of the definitions I have quoted? Two of these three definitions imply that goal or problem exploration would serve to delimit the field. Would this actually be the case?

Study discloses that current service boundaries are in fact understandable only in cultural, social, and historical terms, since they reflect attitudes towards deviance and need, the point at which the culture has changed its approaches to various categories of illness or problems, the dynamics of the development of many professions, and the growth of knowledge and technology (7). It is not surprising that boundaries do not coincide with people's illnesses and problems. To some extent, all illness and malfunctioning affects all areas of life, and a variety of intervention systems could be brought to bear on most serious difficulties. This is documented by a substantial body of research, which shows the extent to which people who have significant problems in one area of living (for example, dependency or illness) often have concurrent problems and are receiving treatment in other areas (for example, anti-social behavior). While recognizing that an act of will can change neither the boundaries of intervention systems nor the ways in which people's problems are divided up within them, since fundamental social control mechanisms are at work, we must nonetheless ask in which direction we are to move, given the available degrees of freedom. To put it another way, to the extent that rational planning is involved—and it is—what would knowledge and experience suggest?

A slightly oversimplified version of the widespread debate over the proper function of the outpatient mental health clinic and its relationship to a state hospital system may provide an approach to this question (7). Some deduce from the evidence available that the public defines much deviance as eccentricity but that when deviance becomes intolerable the public sees it as severe illness and copes with it by rejection. In their view, the public "demands" a separate and essentially isolated mental hospital and aftercare system and believes that to place the less ill and the intolerable deviants within the same system will cause adjustment difficulties rather than facilitate services to all the mentally ill. Others argue from the same evidence that clinicians can affect change in public attitudes and in the fate of the mentally ill by demonstrating in their stance and in their organizational decisions their belief in the continuity of all conduct from the normal to the most disturbed. Organizing for community integration of the ill and for reintegrating those who have been hospitalized affects expectations and changes rejection patterns.

At this point, some of those in the debate introduce still another issue. They ask whether the problems, techniques, and methods of working with the severely mentally ill on a day-night hospital or aftercare basis, or possibly in the hospital, are not different from the tasks in an outpatient clinic that is concerned with adjustment problems, normal role performance, and the discomfort of the mildly or moderately maladjusted. They see a need for separate hospital, outpatient clinic, and aftercare systems, apart from community adult and child guidance clinics. To the argument that there are coherence and unity in all outpatient services they answer that community sanctions are quite different in the two systems. Where a client is at the point of requiring hospitalization or is on aftercare or day-hospital status, the psychiatrist functions with a degree of responsibility and community leverage quite different from that which he exercises when a mildly uncomfortable adult does not return to a clinic after an interview.

From still another point of view, a community mental health center should be dedicated to the promotion and maintenance of mental health in a community. It should involve many disciplines, and the doctor should play a central role only when the issue of medical responsibility is primary. The center would not, per se, be an integral part of a medical network.

Without elaborating these positions any further, it is possible to state that a discussion of boundary issues should include certain topics:

1 the public's view of a given social problem, disability, or need;

2 the expert professional view of this problem;

3 the culmination of these views in a social decision as to what a service is to accomplish;

4 the available sanctions or socially defined leverage for implementing this decision;

5 the conceptualization of the intervention system and the

availability of knowledge and skill about how this concept can be translated into the appropriate service;

6 the extent to which knowledge and skills must differ and thus demand unique training and induction methods, as well as specialized organizations and even statutory supports, for adequate development and implementation.

I have elsewhere summarized all this in the following terms: "These listings reduce themselves to a *need-diagnosis* concept (a definition of the phenomena being treated), a definition of what is known about *how* to serve or treat (treatment method), and the public social context and *sanctions* as they affect the decisions" (7).

How does this apply to community psychiatry and community mental health? It is in the realm of direct service that this field, whatever it is called, makes its most serious bid as an intervention system. In response to human maladjustment and malfunctioning, to human unhappiness, disturbance, and antisocial behavior, modern society has developed a variety of forms of institutional intervention. Considering such factors as community sanction and leverage and available clusters of knowledge and skill, it is possible to list several major intervention systems. Each of these has developed subsystems. Income maintenance assures the economic minimum through a variety of transfer payment devices such as social security and assistance. Courts and correctional services cope with behavior assumed to justify severe sanctions (probation) and, if necessary, deprivation of liberty. Medicine is the core discipline of the medical-clinical group, and there are interrelated subsystems for both physical medicine and psychiatry. (Needless to say, the term "medical" is broadly used here.) The general counseling, guidance, and social services, which provide programs from child welfare to family guidance, may draw on psychiatry, medicine, education, and other disciplines, but they are primarily based on social work and psychology rather than on medicine.

Although this list is tentative and incomplete, it does suggest that the distinguishing characteristic of the medical-clinical group is alignment with medicine. The public sanctions a system of helping in which the doctor, perhaps one of several specialists, is

the central responsible figure. The many segments of this system
are connected by the core professional discipline and by continuity
of medical responsibility. There is an important body of knowledge, experience, and professional ethics related to this work, and
it is buttressed by organizations and agencies.

Moreover, professional knowledge and experience in the psychiatric subsection of the medical-clinical group document the
necessity of many of the new trends in organization: decentraliza-
tion, emphasis on community-based treatment, continuity of care
from clinic to general hospital to psychiatric hospital to halfway
house to aftercare. Operational requirements are such that this
system must have strong social science and social practice support
and its staff must be drawn from a variety of interrelated professions. What emerges reshapes psychiatric practice and contributes
to its potential; and it has led to the addition of the word "community" in the terms "community mental health" and "community
psychiatry." (Dr. Mechanic's paper, [see below, Chapter 11]
dramatizes the urgency of assuring the place of this broad
component in the psychiatric subsystem.)

When the question is raised, as it was earlier, whether those in
a mental health clinic should be identified with the hospital
system serving the more severely ill, the relevance of the general
system of counseling, guidance and social services as an alternative
should be considered. For here is the clue to the boundary of the
medical-clinic group in its psychiatric subspecialty: Where medical control and responsibility are required for an intervention and
where public definitions, self-perceptions, and institutional rules
support it, the service should be provided under the auspices of
community psychiatry.

(Needless to say, the definition of medicine used here notes, as
do Duhl and Mechanic, the interaction between individual and
environment, psyche and social systems. Unlike Mechanic, I
would not separate out as "unscientific" the value choices embodied in the current practice of an intervention system. A system
is characterized by knowledge, skill, and value stances, and its use
is thereby defined.)

If we follow this line of reasoning, the distinctions noted at the
outset between community psychiatry and case psychiatry no

longer hold. A possible exception, however, may be the private practitioner who, in his office, acts as though a patient has no identity other than that manifested within the office and will need no services or institutional supports for change other than those that exist in the psychiatrist's private sanctum.

Duhl reminds us that "Disease must be seen not as an independent entity but rather something that is intricately tied to the individual, the host of the disease, and to the particular social setting within which both the disease and the individual's development occur . . . . [At] some point or another, as a result of a very special combination of circumstances of host, environment, and the significant etiological factors, the disease is said to begin" (5).

In this sense, all psychiatry is or should be part of the system of community psychiatry. To consider relationship contexts in working on a case basis is to intervene in systems that extend beyond the psyche of any single individual: this is true even where the formulation of a case is initially genetic or biological. And it is inevitable in dealing with broad areas of social deviance, in response to which, as Dr. Mechanic points out, the community enacts, through the symbolism of labeling, a variety of value choices and social control patterns.

The bias of community psychiatry is toward intervention designed to affect populations. When a multidisciplinary team is involved, primary and secondary preventive measures and interventions (in the public health sense of the term) may include direct environmental manipulations. Such a team may seek indirectly to affect the individual's environment through staff training and consultation, among other education endeavors, and through contributions to administration or organization policy. But here the aspirations are greater than the achievements. The essential point is that the same professional knowledge is basic both to individual case measures and to broad interventions. Were this not so, the two could not be described as parts of one intervention system.

Thus, the realm of community psychiatry may be considered to encompass a total inpatient and outpatient treatment network, case-finding arrangements, a referral system, many types of com-

munity-based service, the provision of plans for case integration
and continuity of care, and the means for assuring adequate ties
with the general medical system. In addition, community psychiatry, as do all intervention systems, needs administrative
structures and policy, planning and social action arrangements,
to help it develop and protect its domain, assure support, and
implement new ideas.

Community psychiatry is involved in other types of activity as
well. It can and does contribute to measures, described in public
health terms as primary and secondary prevention, that are designed to decrease the frequency of medical illness and maladjustment. A common example is providing guidance to parents in
child-rearing practices. Some community psychiatrists now contribute to policies and programs in secondary institutions (schools,
industry, the Peace Corps) whose aim is to maximize individual
development and adjustment. Others have contributed to the
formulation of broad social policy with regard, for example, to air
raid drills and the search for peace.

Obviously, other social groupings and professions also enter
into these realms of activity. Substantial questions have been
raised as to the competence of community psychiatry in these
areas, and as to whether members of the community psychiatry
team could not better pursue these goals in other ways.

It may be possible, eventually, to distinguish between the
activities which should be carried out under the auspices of
community psychiatry and those in which the community psychiatrist should participate as expert or consultant, perhaps under
other than psychiatric or even medical administrative structures.
It is too soon to spell out principles for making this distinction,
but the central question is the relevance of available professional
knowledge, competence, and sanction. At many points, of course,
the community psychiatry professional is citizen, not expert.

Much could, in fact, be said about the knowledge and competence required for any community psychiatric practice. In general, performance of service network tasks demands clinical
competence supplemented by a social science approach to case
analysis and intervention and to organizational planning. Policy
and prevention tasks, on the other hand, even when narrowly

defined or when performed in support of more direct service, would seem to demand a mastery of the clinical knowledge unique to this medical specialty (but not necessarily demand a high level of clinical competence), with more emphasis on organizational theory and change theory. Since the total intervention system is manned by representatives of several professions and disciplines, these requirements, despite their breadth, are not unreasonable.

Shared clinical knowledge and identification with a common task enable community psychiatry staffs in the direct service network and teams in the broader assignments jointly to contribute to a total effort.

In suggesting a community psychiatry intervention system whose activities range from treatment to formulation of some aspects of public policy, we may seem to be condoning some of the definitions we rejected earlier. Focusing on the core knowledge, skills, values, and sanctions growing out of the psychiatric base, however, facilitates the designation of boundaries. The most difficult area to delimit, that involving broad policy extrapolations, will actually prove to be self-limiting as the community learns to make distinctions for itself.

COMMUNITY MENTAL HEALTH

There are those who would assign all the broader so-called preventive and enhancement activities to the realm of what they would define as community mental health. But this designation is too vague to be practical. To the extent that community psychiatric knowledge is the core of an intervention or action, the activities relevant to that intervention should be considered part of the community psychiatry intervention system.

The phrase "community mental health" program or activity may be more usefully employed to designate that more general coalition of people and organizations which comes together around social goals and which consists of many loosely interrelated components from several intervention systems and social institutions joined together for the purpose. This occasional coming together of laymen and members of several professions has its significance, but it is something other than community psychiatric practice.

The assurance of the resources, stimulation, relationships, serv-ices, and protections necessary for adequate, and even optimal, social participation and realization of individual potentialities is a widely held social goal. Achievement of this goal would have implications, for example, for general medicine, psychiatry, law enforcement, and family welfare agencies. Human rights legisla-tion is, to be sure, a mental health promotion, but it holds equally significant implications for attitudes toward law, citizen partici-pation in government, physical medicine, income maintenance programs, and upgrading of educational motivations and individ-ual capacity. Whether one considers all this as generalized primary prevention in the public health sense, as "preventive medicine," as positive mental health, or as the search for the good society and the social justice outlined by philosophers, it is certain that no boundary claimed here by any one profession or group of professions will be taken seriously.

These are desirable forms of developmental provision in many fields, to be sought because they enrich life and contribute to social goals and the realization of widely held values. These goals include income maintenance and provision of educational oppor-tunities, leisure-time resources, day-care and homemaker facili-ties, a specified level of housing, cultural opportunities, and public health protection. Each represents a projection from strongly held values and a societal definition of what people of a given era require. Each is believed to contribute to the good life. None is adequately formulated if developed only as a means of avoiding pathology, illness, and maladjustment. The prevention concept is inadequate: what should be considered are provision and enhancement. What is needed are best seen as social resources and utilities.

The subgoals in these fields have been elaborated by their participants, and mutual planning is now being carried on through so-called "planning coalitions." Where does psychiatry enter?

The mental health movement is one of several arenas in which such coalitions are formed. During the 1950's, it became an increasingly popular arena for this purpose because of a general tendency in our culture to humanize and even to psychologize our approach to most social institutions. We now stress such goals as individual adjustment, happiness, and enhancement, whereas, at one time, the only issue was adequate and efficient production.

However, just as mental health represents far more than the opposite of mental illness, this generalized movement represents more than community psychiatry. Community psychiatrists make a major contribution, but non-clinicians—informed citizens, clergymen, educators, rehabilitation personnel, and others—play their parts. The impact of primary (family) and secondary institutions (church, school, job, club) on human adjustment and functioning is of particular significance.

In this sense, the community mental health movement is just emerging, and its future is uncertain. The knowledge, skill, and acceptability of this activity should not be overestimated, nor should the number of its accomplishments. Parallel goals are to some extent defined as substantially in other fields—religion, politics, adult recreation—and experiments are being carried out with organizational vehicles that are based on locale (neighborhood organization) rather than on professional identity. Many on the community psychiatry team utilize these other outlets in their search for contributions to the good life.

To put it in different terms, the boundaries of community mental health's preventive role are broad and inclusive. Despite customary usage, community mental health is more a social movement or goal formulation than an intervention system. It is one of a series of overlapping areas in which those seeking the good life act. It has few claims to monopoly, or even to success, and its adherents wisely hedge their bets by trying a variety of outlets. There are, in fact, indications that our society may be tending away from this sort of approach to social action rationale, as is evidenced by the recent emphasis on "poverty" rather than on "maladjustment." None of this is too alarming as a cultural phenomenon. The basic task of community psychiatry remains, since the heart of the *expertise* and know-how is in the community psychiatry system. This system seeks to establish the character of its *expertise* and then seeks to utilize it in the total range of its activities.

This analysis has been presented with full appreciation of the fact that federal statutes do not define community mental health and other terms as they have been defined here or elsewhere in the relevant literature. We face inconsistency and illogic: community mental health centers should actually be called community psychiatric centers, and perhaps in the future they will be. But why not clarify the policy and then choose the words?

The lesson of a boundaries discussion, in short, is that we must clarify the nature of knowledge and competence at a given moment, package it in efficient and effective fashion, and relate it to the major value choices facing society. This is certainly something that people engaged in community psychiatry will want to do.

References

1 BELLAK, LEOPOLD, ED. *Handbook of Community Psychiatry and Community Mental Health.* New York, Grune & Stratton, 1964.

2 CAPLAN, G. "Community Psychiatry—Introduction and Overview." In *Concepts of Community Psychiatry*, edited by Stephen E. Goldston. Washington, D.C., U.S. Dept. of Health, Education, and Welfare, 1965.

3 CAPLAN, G., ED. *Prevention of Mental Disorders in Children.* New York, Basic Books, 1961.

4 CUMMING, ELAINE. "Allocation of Care to the Mentally Ill, American Style." In *Systems of Social Control*, edited by Mayer N. Zald. Atherton Press. Publication pending.

5 DUHL, L. J. "The Psychiatric Evolution." In *Concepts of Community Psychiatry*, edited by Stephen E. Goldston. Washington, D.C., U.S. Dept. of Health, Education, and Welfare, 1965.

6 GOLDSTON, S. E. *Selected Definitions.* Bethesda, Maryland, National Institute of Mental Health, 1963. Mimeographed.

7 KAHN, A. J. Boundaries. Publication pending.

8 KAHN, A. J. Case channeling. Publication pending.

9 KAHN, A. J. *Planning Community Services for Children in Trouble.* New York, Columbia Univ. Press, 1963.

10 KAHN, A. J. Social work and the control of delinquency. *Social Work,* April, 1965, pp. 3–13.

Ten

Law and Psychiatry
An Approach to *Rapprochement*

FRANCIS A. ALLEN, LL.B.

T HE relations of law and psychiatry have rarely been se-
rene, and they have sometimes been tempestuous. There is
nothing new in this. The literature of mutual castigation is of
ancient lineage; it began to appear almost as soon as psychiatry
emerged from its antecedents as a distinct body of knowledge
and practice. This interprofessional warfare is, no doubt, a
phenomenon of some significance. If we fully understood the
dynamics of these controversies, we should probably know more
about ourselves and about the social roles of the legal and
psychiatric professions. Being a veteran of more discussions
across disciplinary lines than I can now enumerate, I have often
witnessed and, indeed, participated in these acrimonious exchanges. I have come to suspect that they perform an almost
ritualistic function. Ritual has its uses, and I am not insensitive to
the satisfactions to be gained from verbal aggression. Accordingly, I do not wish to express too grave alarm over the fact that,
on occasion, lawyers and psychiatrists are prone to speak harshly
to each other.

On the other hand, this ritualistic acrimony in which our
professions have indulged is a luxury, and it has become apparent

to many that it is an expensive luxury. For psychiatry and the law are increasingly involved in problems of mutual concern and of concern to the community at large. These problems urgently require our united attention, and they will not wait for lawyers and psychiatrists to resolve all the issues of theory and of values that now divide them. Fundamental issues must be attended to, but in the meantime we need to seek accommodations in the interest of attaining practical objectives. We have had enough experience with interdisciplinary efforts to know that such accommodations are possible and beneficial.

As I have listened to the dialogue between law and psychiatry over the years, it has seemed to me that we have often become entangled in false issues, or we have, at least, magnified certain differences into unrealistic proportions. I do not for a moment suggest that all our controversies have no substantial basis, that they are purely verbal in character, or that all that is required to bring harmony out of discord is a prescription from the semanticist. On the other hand, it has occurred to me that some of our mutual irritations stem less from our differences than from the similarity of our objectives. For in a sense it is surely true that psychiatry and the law possess certain broad objectives in common. Both are humane disciplines in that each is concerned with the human animal in a social context, both are committed to the realization of constructive human potentialities, and both aspire to the attainment of a fuller humanity. Shared objectives, however, do not necessarily guarantee harmony. They may, in fact, encourage discord when differences develop as to means and secondary goals. As Professor Paul Freund has observed in another context, we are likely to feel greater frustration and irritation when confronted by the heretic than by the infidel (5).

However this may be, it is clear that certain factors have persistently obstructed fruitful and needed collaboration of law and psychiatry. No factor is more important in this regard than the controversy that has raged for more than a century over the legal tests to determine the criminal responsibility of persons afflicted by mental illness. No other issue has received so much attention or been so productive of acrimony as the debate over the M'Naghten rules (8) and the related legal formulations (3,

4). These controversies and the attitudes produced in consequence have diverted attention from other basic problems and
have impeded fruitful interchange on those occasions when other
problems have been made the subject of discussion. I am far from
denying that the tests of criminal responsibility are important as
to matters both of theory and of practice. Yet it is also true that,
even if one confines his attention to the administration of criminal
justice, there is a range of problems involving mental disorder
that cumulatively are fully as important, and perhaps more
important, than the formulation of the tests of responsibility (2).
One can scarcely call for a moratorium in the debate over
M'Naghten, Durham, and the other proposed legal formulae. But
with advantage we can recognize the importance of extending the
scope of the interdisciplinary dialogue to encompass other issues
and problem areas.

    In the past, contacts between lawyers and psychiatrists have
involved only a small fraction of the membership of each
profession performing a rather limited range of professional
functions. These contacts have not only been limited in type and
frequency, but they have often been abrasive in character. The
existing relations between law and psychiatry are the product of
these underlying facts. There is considerable evidence, however,
that the range and frequency of interprofessional contacts will
increase in the future and that they will involve much more than,
for example, the adversary posture of lawyer and psychiatrist in
the criminal prosecution or civil-commitment proceeding. The
prospect of such increasing encounters is a source of both hope
and concern. It is a source of hope because, clearly, solution of
many important social problems requires, or would at least be
advanced by, intelligent co-operative efforts by both professions.
It is a source of concern because, unless these encounters are
managed with wisdom and forbearance, they will obstruct rather
than promote solution of the community's problems. The avoid-
ance of the danger which this concern reflects must, therefore, be
regarded as a pressing responsibility of both professional groups.
In these remarks I shall attempt to do two things. First, I shall
endeavor to identify some of the values expressed by the law and
some of the presuppositions of the legal order which are com-

monly misunderstood or imperfectly understood by therapists and which have been the source of friction and controversy in the past. Second, I shall attempt to identify a number of particular areas in which collaborative efforts might produce constructive gains for the community.

Recent years have produced considerable literature that discusses the values implicit in the practice of psychotherapy. Some of this literature has launched a vigorous attack on the concepts of "mental health" expressed in some mental health movements. A number of writers have challenged the integrity of the concept and have asserted that many proposed definitions of "mental health" serve simply to cloak the economic, political, social, or moral bias of the person employing the term (*13, 14, 19*). It is not my present purpose to become engaged in these polemics. I am required to say, however, that development of constructive relations between law and psychiatry is obstructed by certain implicit conflicts of values. Moreover, these conflicts are rendered more difficult to identify and resolve because of the propensity of some psychiatrists to conceive of their discipline as an expression of scientific neutrality, wholly removed from and unconcerned with moral values. It must, indeed, be true that many therapeutic procedures are applied in circumstances that do not call into being any contestable issues of moral choice. Speaking as a layman, however, it seems almost selfevident that any discipline that proposes in its practice to affect the interpersonal relations of human beings must inevitably be deeply involved in issues of moral and ethical significance. To a layman, the comment of Professor Perry London appears cogent and persuasive:

Moral considerations may dictate, in large part, how the therapist defines his client's need, how he operates in the therapeutic situation, how he defines "treatment," and "cure," and even "reality."

Many psychotherapists are poignantly aware of this. Students of mental health find that it is difficult even to *define* such terms as "health," "illness," "normality," without some reference to morals; and worse still, they cannot discuss the proper treatment of what they have defined without recognizing and involving their own moral commitments (*7*).

The senses in which and the degree to which psychiatry can hold itself aloof from value judgments that are of concern both to patients and to the community are large and important questions. I would also suggest that the questions become even more important when psychiatry moves out of the consulting rooms of private practitioners and seeks aggressively to expand the scope and range of its services in the community. For it is clear that however "neutral" the attitudes of psychiatrists toward basic value issues may be, the community, which is the recipient of psychiatric services, is far from neutral. The community possesses a morality and a scale of values. Indeed, the community of which we speak is not only a community of persons; it is a community of values. The system of values expressed by any society defies full and precise description. The very notion of community presupposes a measure of consensus about what is right and wrong, useful and harmful, beautiful and ugly. But in a dynamic society diversity as well as unity will be encountered. No one needs to be told that in our time society encompasses conflicting values and that flux and change are the order of the day. No group seeking greater involvement with the community and offering solutions for community problems can escape involvement with the community's values. In this encounter interaction is to be anticipated. Psychiatry may expect both to alter the community and its values and, in turn, to be altered and influenced by its involvement with the community.

These matters are relevant to the consideration of the relations between law and psychiatry, for the law not only provides important evidence of what the community values are but is itself a source of values. The law, therefore, constitutes a part of the social context in which programs of community psychiatry must operate. This is completely apparent when statutory provisions impose immediate and practical limitations on the development of community mental health programs. No one can doubt the relevance of legal limitations that establish salary scales at levels too low to attract competent professionals to staff public health or welfare agencies; that create a structure of clinical and welfare facilities inadequate in number or size and bearing no rational relationship to each other; that, in short, obstruct or prevent the devising of a system capable of identifying needs and supplying the range of services required. Even when conceived in this way, the law may be seen as reflecting community values. If public health and welfare programs do not receive adequate financial support from government, the community is tacitly testifying that other governmental functions are more important—highways, education, national defense, or perhaps the construction of convention halls (9). Statutes that obstruct an effective organization of services may reflect community indifference and the strength of vested interests.

But this does not reach the heart of the matter. Statutory provisions and administrative practices relating to health and welfare can be amended and modified, given the requisite intelligence, energy, and will to effect reform. What is more significant in appraising the relations of law and psychiatry are certain fundamental attitudes expressed in the law toward the values of individual liberty and volition and the exercise of the coercive powers of government. The nature of law has been the subject of disputation by lawyers and philosophers at least from the time of ancient Greece. No comprehensive definition of law has proved universally acceptable, and jurisprudential debates on this basic issue are as characteristic of the modern era as of former times. For present purposes it is not necessary to attempt any such comprehensive definition. It seems sufficient to point out that, from any point of view, the law in many of its most important aspects is concerned with the power of the organized community to achieve its objectives and the impact of that power on individual members of the community. That law is concerned with the exercise of the public force is made manifest by our usage of such phrases as "law enforcement." All organized communities, with greater or lesser effectiveness, employ the force of the community to attain such basic objectives as the security of persons and possessions and the defense of the group from aggression by other groups. It is only man-in-society who can realize the full extent and range of human capacities, and the benefits of social living require the wise administration of the community's power.

But the effective accomplishment of community purposes is only one part of the law's concern. As men of the twentieth century have had ample opportunity to observe, the power of the state is capable of being employed in ways that are antagonistic to the individual and his interests and that thwart the development of human potentialities. The law of a free society, therefore, is concerned not only to unleash the effective power of the community but to limit it and to contain its use for purposes conceived by a majority of citizens as beneficial. Most legal prescriptions that seek to regulate human behavior display this dual aspect. Thus a criminal statute defines, let us say, the offense of larceny and provides for a range of penalties that may be imposed in the event of conviction. Such a statute authorizes the public force to be brought to bear against the individual in the interest of attaining a proper community objective: the security of possessions. But the statute not only releases the power of the state; it limits state authority. For the law is also saying that no man may be punished for larceny *unless* he has behaved in the ways specified in the statute. Even primitive legal formulations such as the *lex talionis* take on new significance when seen in this light. Thus the formula of "an eye for an eye; a tooth for a tooth" represents more than a cry for tribal vengeance; for, as has often been remarked, the rule avoids the forfeiture of a life for an eye, or an eye for a tooth.

The history of Anglo-American law displays the slow development of measures and tactics for the containment of state power and for the protection of individuals from the deliberate or negligent abuse of official authority. There is no more important product of this historical development than the adversary system of justice; and yet few features of the legal order have been approached with less sympathy and understanding by members of the behavioral disciplines. Some sense of the importance of the adversary system can be gained if one observes the judicial procedures it eventually replaced. The great state trials during the Tudor regime in England revealed a system of criminal justice dedicated to the dominant objective of liquidating or incapacitating persons suspected of being enemies of the ruling house. Defendants in treason prosecutions were not permitted to see a copy of the charges against them before trial. They were not generally permitted to call witnesses in their own defense. They were not, in general, entitled to retain counsel to speak for them at the trials even when they possessed ample financial resources to hire counsel. Whatever contributions such a system made to the stability of the state following the ravages of the Wars of the Roses, its costs were eventually seen to be extravagant. Not only did the system produce human tragedies as a result of the conviction and punishment of innocent persons, but, since it was incapable of adequately distinguishing the guilty from the innocent, it allowed persons who constituted genuine threats to the security of the state to escape the restraining hand of state power.

The adversary system is predicated on wholly different assumptions. Whenever the state proposes to deprive a person of such possessions as his liberty, his life, or his status as a parent, the case for the exercise of state power must be clearly made. Moreover, the person proceeded against is permitted and, indeed, encouraged to challenge such assertions of state authority by any proper means, including challenges to the evidence produced by the moving party and the introduction of countervailing evidence. The essence of the adversary system is challenge (10). It serves as a continuing reminder to those clothed with state authority that their powers must be exercised within the limits prescribed by the community. It expresses the shrewd insight that those possessed of power are prone to laxness and excess unless subjected to effective challenge and supervision. The validity of this insight is confirmed by the fact that inefficiency and pathology tend to develop in those areas of judicial administration in which the adversary system has broken down. These include the small-crimes courts where effective challenge to the state is not made because the impoverished accused rarely are represented by counsel at the hearings, and because the action of such courts is infrequently subjected to appellate scrutiny. One may also point to the juvenile courts where the absence of a vigorous adversary process reveals that even members of the behavioral disciplines at times are susceptible to carelessness or worse when freed from the stimulus of challenge and effective supervision (15).

There is no question but that the adversary system entails costs. Challenges to the testimony of the state's witnesses may sometimes result in the discrediting of valid, as well as invalid, evidence. It is also true that certain features of judicial proceedings associated with, but not of the essence of, the adversary system cry for reform. And yet, the adversary system is vital to the preservation of our basic political values. I see as yet no evidence to support the confident forecasts of a generation ago that the adversary system is an anachronism scheduled for a speedy demise. On the contrary, recent decisions of the Supreme Court of the United States suggest an expansion and strengthening of the system (*18*). As psychiatry moves into the community, it is likely to become involved in the adversary process with increasing frequency. The behavioral disciplines can make an important contribution to the free society if, in the years ahead, their members confront the adversary system with tolerance and understanding.

The modern age has presented problems of liberty in new and complex forms. As all men who have grown to maturity in our time are aware, the traditional threats to the free society are still very much a part of the twentieth-century world: the ruler disposed to seize tyrannical powers; the political adventurer bent upon a *coup d'état;* or the rise of an unresponsive and irresponsible bureaucratic establishment. But new problems of individual liberty have also emerged which, even if less dramatic, nevertheless produce extraordinary difficulties for public policy. I am referring principally to the problems of individual liberty growing out of the use of the coercive powers of government to achieve goals of therapy and rehabilitation. These problems are difficult, first, because obviously there are some situations in which state powers must be employed for the institutional commitment of persons for care and treatment. The problem thus becomes the more complex one of articulating sound principles for the uses of such power rather than denying its legitimacy outright. These problems are difficult, also, because even when measures or proposals for so-called civil commitment do in fact impinge upon the basic political values of individual liberty and volition, they may reflect elevated motives entirely different from those expressed in other traditional threats to liberty. These measures, even the most unwise, often express a sincere desire to provide help and care for persons assumed to be in need of such services. They are often advanced by groups who claim immunity from the usual forms of legal restraint and who are likely to insist that professionalism and a devotion to science provide sufficient protection against unwarranted invasion of individual rights (*1*). Obviously, this is an area of important concern to both law and psychiatry and calls for serious and forthright discussion.

The past half-century has seen the enactment of a substantial body of legislation authorizing the civil commitment of persons in order to achieve therapeutic or rehabilitative goals. This includes not only the usual measures for the hospitalization of the mentally ill but a whole range of other measures, including the sexual-psychopath laws, the defective-delinquent laws, and the laws for the compulsory commitment of narcotic addicts. There have also been proposals for the commitment of alcoholics for care and treatment. Experience with much of this legislation provides grounds for reasonable concern. The administration of some such laws, particulary the sexual psychopath legislation, raises the psychopath laws, the defective-delinquent laws, and the laws for indeterminate incarceration. Does the state of modern scientific knowledge permit the selection of persons for commitment with reasonable certainty and without the risk of error? However this question is answered in the abstract, it is clear that in actual practice many persons have been deprived of their liberty under the authority of these laws who do not represent serious dangers to the community. Indeed, it is fair to say that these laws have been used, perhaps predominantly, to rid society of persons constituting nuisances to the community rather than dangers (*11*). Interestingly enough, precisely the same point has been made in a recent study of prisoners confined in England under statutes authorizing extended periods of preventive detention (*16*). Once the subject is committed, a second fundamental question arises. Does any therapy exist or is the state in a position to supply a therapeutic regimen likely to effect cures or substantial improvement of the persons incarcerated? If the answer is no, then these measures, in fact, perform only an incapacitative, not a therapeutic, function. Ironically, even the function of incarceration may be badly performed, for often the institutions in which such persons are confined provide an environment less humane and more destructive than that existing in the prisons and penitentiaries of the state. Today proposals for compulsory commitment of narcotic addicts are being enthusiastically advanced as an alternative to the absurdities and inhumanities associated with traditional efforts to reduce the incidence of narcotic addiction through the agencies of the criminal law. It is not difficult to understand and sympathize with the search for more rational measures in this area. But the danger that civil commitment will differ from criminal incarceration chiefly as to the label applied is clear and present; and the danger is not avoided by hopes that confinement of addicts in institutions called "hospitals" rather than "prisons" will result in new knowledge being gained for the effective treatment of narcotic addiction. It is not professional pride that leads me to advance the following proposition: With all of their weaknesses, the agencies of the legal order are more efficient in locking persons up than the behavioral disciplines are in curing and rehabilitating them. The rehabilitative and therapeutic ideal is singularly vulnerable to debasement and corruption when it becomes too intimately associated with the coercive powers of the state. One prime example of this phenomenon is the tendency of measures designed to achieve therapeutic goals to perform, in fact, the function of incapacitative confinement.

Thus far in these remarks, I have been speaking of the relations of law and psychiatry in the language of limitation and restraint. Obviously this is only part of the story, and brief attention needs now to be given to areas in which law and psychiatry can fruitfully unite their efforts to expand the quality and range of community services.

Recently, while glancing through some literature associated with the community psychiatry movement, I encountered two statements which to me were arresting and evocative. The paper in question asserted that "The present day institutional features of psychotherapy are primarily congenial to middle-class life styles" (12). And again, "But—and here is the heart of the problem—the techniques that low-income clients believe in are different from those that the middle-class practitioner believes in" (12). I am in no position, of course, to evaluate these remarks; but they at least suggest that the problem of devising services and techniques appropriate and useful to the lower classes of our communities is one common to both the legal and the psychiatric professions. The law, at least, has been insensitive to these problems too long. There is mounting evidence that many of our welfare programs do not reach persons on the lowest social and economic planes of our society. The law, perhaps in common with psychiatry, has been imprisoned within the middle-class stereotype. We have found it difficult to understand the ways of life in the culture of poverty, and accordingly our measures have failed to produce the anticipated consequences. The influence of the middle-class stereotype and the failure of legislators to understand the forms of family organization prevailing in the deprived areas of our large cities have rendered largely irrelevant much of the discussion now going forward in several states on the issue of supplying contraceptive services to persons on the relief rolls. The facts would seem to be that the incidence of illegitimacy in the slum areas of our cities is in some sense the product of the poverty and deprivation that characterize these communities. Moreover, the birth of unwanted children and children for whom no adequate provision can be made is a cause of new poverty, which prevents the persons involved from rising to levels of life that make family living in the middle-class style possible. There is obviously a vicious circle here that must be broken. Other examples abound. In most states, legislatures seeking to reduce complications in the property relations associated with the family have abolished the practice of common-law marriage. There is surely a case to be made for such legislation, but the losses in the flexibility of the law fall with disproportionate impact on members of our subcultures, who adhere to different traditions of family formation and who are often ignorant of the requirements of valid marriage understood as a matter of course by persons reared in middle-class surroundings (*17*).

Whether the experience gained by either profession in extending its concerns across the lines of status and class will prove transferable to the other, I do not know. In any event, there may be various points at which the services of each profession may be made more effective if rendered in association with those of the other. Legal-aid services for persons unable to hire counsel have, of course, been provided on an organized basis for many decades and informally for a much longer period. There is a growing appreciation among lawyers of the importance of these services and an awareness of their present inadequacy. That legal problems produce stress and anxiety in destitute family groups cannot be doubted. It also seems clear that their proper solution may often make important contributions to the material quality of the life of such families, to the proper functioning of the family unit, and to the emotional well-being of its members. A comprehensive attack on the problems of a problem family may require the services of lawyers as well as social workers and doctors; and experiments providing such a range of services are now going forward in several localities across the nation. I also believe that the establishment of legal-aid clinics in our prisons might well make positive contributions to the rehabilitation of many prisoners. I am not primarily concerned with providing legal assistance to the prisoner who is attempting to win his release in the courts; but, even here, professional assistance might contribute to the improved administration of justice. I am chiefly concerned with relieving the prisoner of the distress produced by legal problems during his period of incarceration. These may include questions of family law or difficulties experienced by the prisoner's family in receiving relief or other welfare allotments. It is also true that the prisoner's legitimate property interests may be invaded while he is in confinement and unable effectively to assert his rights. Legal services have long been recognized as an important morale factor by the military forces, and this experience may have direct application to our penal institutions. However diverse the approaches of the law and psychiatry to the goal of rehabilitation, the goal is common to both. And the contributions of each may enhance the effectiveness of the other.

Surely one of the most important areas of mutual concern is that involving the abused and neglected child and the termination of parental rights. Nothing less than a revolution in legal conceptions of the interests of children has occurred (6). At the common law the right of the father to the custody of the child was virtually absolute. And this right was not accompanied by even the legally enforceable obligation of the father to provide support for the child. The alteration of the older views and the recognition of the child as the object of the law's special and particular concern is one of the triumphs of nineteenth-century humanitarianism. The triumph, of course, is far from complete. It is one thing to pay obeisance to the formula that, when considering issues involving the care and custody of a child, our decision must be determined by the best interests of the child. It is quite another to discover where the child's best interests lie. It is still another to implement the decision when made. Nor can any such formula remove from the agony of decision the feelings of the natural parents or the impact on them and on other family members of the termination of parental rights.

The proper administration of the law relating to the neglected child is a concern of obvious relevance to both professions. It is characterized by an array of the most difficult problems, problems that can be effectively confronted only if there is intelligent collaboration between the legal and behavioral professions. This area is also important because it illustrates admirably what psychiatry will encounter when it seeks greater involvement in the community and, particularly, when it invokes the support of the legal machinery to achieve its goals. Anyone approaching these problem areas will soon be struck by the disorganization of the courts and of private and public agencies dealing with child and family problems. This lack of functional organization impedes the discovery of child abuse and neglect and the reporting of these conditions to the proper authorities when they are discovered. It also interferes with the collection of relevant information upon which decisions must be based. This lack of proper articulation of functions may be encountered within the structure of a single court. In the juvenile court of one large city with which I am familiar the psychiatric clinic sees and interviews only the child brought before the court. Investigation of the home situation and interviews of the parents and other family members are conducted wholly separately by members of the court's social staff. The psychiatric report and the social report are each prepared in ignorance of what the other contains, and both are submitted to the judge without prior communication between the doctor and the social worker. One important contribution the psychotherapist can make to the law, and, incidentally, to the effectiveness of his own services, is a persuasive demonstration of the interrelated quality of problems involving the family with a view to contributing to a more rational allocation of functions among private and official agencies (15).

The child-neglect cases also present to the courts problems of enormous difficulty involving definition of the concept of "neglect" and the proper disposition of cases once neglect, however defined, is established. Traditionally, neglect has been understood as the failure of parents to supply the requisites of physical health and physical survival. Such neglect is demonstrable by what can be seen, heard, touched, and smelled. But it is also clear that neglectful damage can be done to the child and to the interests of the community by the style of child-rearing that obtains in a particular home, and here the problem of communicating with the court is much more demanding and difficult. I believe it is fair to say that psychiatrists and social workers often handle the problems of communication in court badly. These failures stem from a variety of causes. In part, they may reflect the feeling that persuasive communication to a lay tribunal is uncongenial to the therapist's role. More frequently, they represent the fact that the expert witness has no sound grasp of what matters are crucial to the court in arriving at its decision, with the result that what is communicated lacks relevance and impact.

But there is a further problem that goes beyond mere communication and articulation, important as these matters undoubtedly are. When psychiatry invokes the powers of the state to be used in ways that profoundly affect human destiny, the community will demand—and, I believe, will properly demand—that a persuasive demonstration be made of the validity of the expert's appraisal and forecast. Often this demonstration will require more than the expression of clinical judgments, however valid. Something in the nature of empirical, quantitative demonstration may sometimes be demanded. This point has been most effectively made by Dr. Andrew S. Watson of the University of Michigan. Doctor Watson has written:

In all of the literature on the foster care of children there is hardly an article which sets forth explicitly the precise reasons, risks, and advantages for disrupting a family unit by placing one or more of its children in foster care. There are many assertions of the effectiveness of this procedure and how helpful it may be, but nowhere can one find data on the why or the how. Nowhere can one check predictions about the use of this procedure, nor does it appear that such material has ever been collected. Preliminary impressions of data from a current research effort would indicate that foster care is utilized on an *ad hoc* basis which would be extremely difficult to justify one way or the other from case records.

Because of the lack of such basic information in this and most other family law areas, when efforts are made by psychiatrists or social workers to alter custody of a child by means of court procedure, they are quite incapable of responding to the judge's request for some kind of evidence to justify the change (*15*).

The present age is one of great challenge to the law and the legal order. Perhaps the most important tasks facing the legal system involve the dual responsibility, first, of making effective use of the new knowledge so that it may contribute to the amelioration of the human condition and improve the quality of human life, and, second, of achieving these goals through means that advance and are compatible with the basic values of a free community. These are tasks for lawyers, judges, and legislators, but they cannot be accomplished by these groups alone. They are, in my judgment, also the goals of the collaboration of law and psychiatry.

References

1 ALLEN, F. A. Criminal justice, legal values and the rehabilitative ideal. *Journal of Criminal Law, Criminology, and Police Science* 50:226, 1958.

2 ALLEN, F. A. The rule of the American Law Institute's Model Penal Code. *Marquette Law Review* 45:494, 1962.

3 AMERICAN LAW INSTITUTE. *Model Penal Code* § 4.01 (Tent. Draft No. 4, 1955).

4 *Durham v. United States*, 214 F.2d 862 (D.C. Cir. 1954).

5 FREUND, P. *On Understanding the Supreme Court*. Boston, Little, Brown, 1949.

6   GILL, T. D. The legal nature of neglect. *National Probation and Parole Association Journal* 6:1, 1960.

7   LONDON, P. The morals of psychotherapy. *Columbia University Forum* 38, Fall, 1961.

8   *M'Naghten's Case*, 10 Cl. and F. 200, Eng. Rep. 718 (1843).

9   NICHOLS, R. S. The influence of economic and administrative factors upon the type and quality of care given to persons with psychological disorders. *Work Papers in Community Mental Health* 1:1, 1963.

10 REPORT OF THE ATTORNEY GENERAL'S COMMITTEE ON POVERTY AND THE ADMINISTRATION OF FEDERAL CRIMINAL JUSTICE. Washington, D.C., 1964.

11 REPORT OF THE ILLINOIS COMMISSION ON SEX OFFENDERS. Springfield, 1953.

12 RIESSMAN, F. *New Approaches to Mental Health Treatment for Labor and Low Income Groups*. National Institute for Labor Education,

13 SWARTZ, L. H. "Mental disease": The groundwork for legal analysis and legislative action. *University of Pennsylvania Law Review* 111:389, 1963.

14 SZASZ, T. S. *Law, Liberty and Psychiatry*. New York, Macmillan, 1963.

15 WATSON, A. S. Family law and its challenge for psychiatry. *Journal of Family Law* 2:71, 1962.

16 WEST, D. J. *The Habitual Offender*. London, Macmillan, 1963.

17 WEYRAUCH, W. O. Informal and formal marriage—an appraisal of trends in family organization. *University of Chicago Law Review* 28:88, 1960.

18 *White v. Maryland*, 373 U.S. 59 (1963).

19 WOOTON, BARBARA. *Social Science and Social Pathology*. London, Allen and Unwin, 1959.

Eleven

Community Psychiatry: Some Sociological Perspectives and Implications

DAVID MECHANIC, PH.D.

C ONCEPTIONS of community psychiatry vary greatly. They range from those that perceive community psychiatry as a new social movement for rehabilitating the sick society to those that contain modest programs for improving facilities already available; from those concerned with preventing the occurrence of mental disorder in entire populations to those concerned with rehabilitating already incapacitated patients; and from those that visualize a variety of new roles for the psychiatrist and other mental health workers to those that fall within traditional concepts of practitioner-patient relationships. Thus it should be clear that, given the ambiguity of the dimensions and limits of community psychiatry, any general discussion is likely to appear false on at least some fronts. Rather than attempt to comment in a general way on the variety of concepts that claim to be community psychiatry, I will attempt to develop from a sociological perspective the issues that have general relevance to a variety of programs and that point out dangers as well as possible advantages of proposed practices.

The considerable recent interest in community psychiatry is an outgrowth of a political and social climate that encourages the maximal use of human potential and of a profound dissatisfaction in some quarters with current psychiatric practice. Psychiatry, whatever its merits and accomplishments, has failed to accept the challenge of severe mental disorder and instead has devoted its major resources toward working with patients of higher socio-economic background with moderate and mild impairments. At the same time, it has been evident that the bulk of the most seriously impaired patients has remained, neglected, in custodial institutions with limited and unimaginative programs; and that much that could, with proper motivation and orientation, be accomplished toward their rehabilitation has been left undone (4).

The failure of hospital psychiatry is more complex than it may seem; and there are various reasons why psychiatry as a profession has not done more for the sickest patients. Since most patients in American custodial institutions are there involuntarily, the psychiatrist is required to adopt a role that is quite foreign to traditional medical practice. Involuntary patients often lack motivation for treatment, and this adds difficulty to an already challenging situation. Moreover, psychiatrists as a group feel little confidence in treating severely disordered patients of lower social class background—patients who are not particularly sophisticated or receptive to psychiatry in the first place. The well-trained psychiatrist who chooses to work in hospital settings, thus sacrificing professional status, money, and psychological comfort, quickly becomes frustrated when he realizes how inappropriate his training and skills are for dealing with large groups of disordered patients. Psychotherapy is not a feasible solution to the problem; yet that is what the psychiatrist has been trained to do and knows how to do best. In addition, the difficulties in obtaining involvement and co-operation from a variety of attendants and nurses, who often wish to maintain their power and to facilitate their own comfort, make the challenge appear insurmountable (22). It is, therefore, not surprising that the psychiatrist leaves the hospital setting to enter private practice, which is consistent with his training and frame of reference and is financially and psychologically more comfortable.

The recent interest in improving facilities for the treatment of the mentally ill results from an increased feeling of professional responsibility for treatment programs in mental hospitals and those within the community (*18*). Before discussing proposals for altering some of the inadequacies of these programs, it is necessary to review some aspects of mental disorder and community processes that are relevant to the disposition of the mentally ill.

THE IDENTIFICATION AND DEFINITION OF THE MENTALLY ILL

"Mental illness" is a particularly slippery concept. We all, of course, can recognize that some persons' behavior, feelings, and communication show so little contact with reality that we can easily agree that they are "sick." However, when we move away from extreme cases, it is far from clear what criteria determine health and illness; and attempts to specify such criteria often reflect ethical, moral, and social judgments. Dr. C. Hardin Branch (*3*), for example, has recently argued that psychiatrists should be allowed to intervene in cases, without legal impediments, if a person can be "considered injurious to himself or others." Examples of what he considers injurious are cases where "the lack of judgment caused by [a person's] mental illness leads him into business enterprises so bizarre that they bankrupt him and his family" or when a professional person "behaved in such a peculiar way that he irrevocably damaged his reputation for continued professional activity." The question, however, is not as simple as it may appear, for objective methods, which allow such determinations to be made in situations where relevant parties disagree, are largely absent. Given the lack of clear and fully objective indicators, the use of involuntary action presents some acute difficulties. Professor Jerome Hall (*13*), an eminent jurist and Distinguished Service Professor of Law at Indiana University, has nicely summarized in his discussion of criminal responsibility the difficulties involved:

The problem of mental disease and criminal responsibility has, therefore, the appearance of utter simplicity. It is merely a matter of finding out which harm-doers had a serious mental disease at the legally relevant time, and the experts in that kind of disease are psychiatrists. . . . In fact, the difficulties run much deeper than that. They inhere in the vagueness of "disease" and in the assumption that mental disease is like physical disease. . . . The only point of relatively substantial agreement seems to be that it is possible and easy to recognize a mental disease which is a very great deviation from the ordinary standard of mental health in a particular culture. This implies that any intelligent person, given the facts, can recognize seriously disordered persons—the conclusion reached by a leading psychiatrist after careful study of the question. . . . He finds that there are only "operational criteria" to guide psychiatrists in this regard, especially that seriously disordered persons create difficult social situations. There is an "urgency" to have them treated: "Society responds to this by legalizing removal of the seriously ill." Thus, it is ordinary social judgment which determines who is psychotic, not any "medical science" that is even remotely like the knowledge used to determine that a person has tuberculosis or malaria.

In defining mental disorder the psychiatrist and the persons concerned may disagree; and such disputes may involve conflicts between liberty and psychiatry, especially if usual legal safeguards are abandoned (29). Since objective criteria in the usual sense do not exist for ascertaining "mental health," expert determinations that are enforced involuntarily upon a person often reflect the use of psychiatry for social control purposes. Implicit in most commitment proceedings is the idea that it is necessary to detain the patient involuntarily in order to protect him or others from danger or injury. But these concepts are poorly specified, and it is not clear whether psychiatrists, in making judgments of danger and injury, adequately weigh the risks of responding to the patient as if he is dangerous against the risks of possible harm resulting from defining and treating him in this way (24, 26). All too often decisions about hospitalization reflect the needs of the community and the reluctance of decision-makers to take professional risks.

Let me emphasize that I am not referring to cases of obvious danger, such as threatened suicide, where most psychiatrists would agree that some form of detention was warranted. I refer primarily to those abundant cases where the patient is involuntarily detained because his actions, in the eyes of the psychiatrist or others, are injurious to the patient's or his family's social standing, reputation, or financial solvency. I am not denying that aberrations exist; nor am I denying that they may have definite genetic and psychological etiologies. I am questioning, however, whether these aberrations truly endanger the community, and whether enforced hospitalization is an adequate mode of approach to such problems.

The concepts of injury and danger, as used in evaluating persons with presumed mental disorders, have some curious social implications. The psychiatrist may come to the conclusion that a person is not acting in his self-interest and is injuring himself and others when he engages in bizarre and irresponsible behavior. The psychiatrist is often called in by interested parties to discredit such persons and their behavior through judgments that assert that the behavior results from a "mental disorder." Thus the psychiatrist, through a medical judgment, may support the social unit by enforcing a particular standard of behavior. What makes such attempts different from the more usual forms of social control is that in the psychiatric case it is presumed that the person can no longer be responsible for his behavior, and thus the action taken is for his own good as well as for the good of other parties. The rationale for taking action is not really dependent on danger or injury (although these words are often used) but rather is based on the presumption that the person cannot exercise judgment in a reasonable way. But the unreasonableness of the patient is defined by the social behavior that is deviant from the morality of the social unit and that others find difficult to understand or tolerate except within a definition of "sickness."

It should be obvious that injury and danger are not the issues, since injurious and dangerous behavior is treated quite differently in contexts where the social behavior is not alien to usual social standards. Thus, although the average drunken driver is probably far more dangerous and injurious to himself and others than most mental patients who are involuntarily detained, detention of a drunken driver for any period of time is rare. Our society also has large numbers of persons who injure their health and threaten their lives through poor health habits and various forms of risk-taking, although they may be fully aware that these practices are dangerous. Similarly, the patient with a heart disorder, diabetes, or some other serious disease may injure his health and threaten his life by not conforming to a medical regimen. Moreover, such behavior may be injurious to his family and employer, since their welfare may be dependent on his health and functioning. Yet it is inconceivable that we would involuntarily detain and forcefully subject to treatment those persons who injure themselves and others by failing to conform to a medical regimen. In short, we do not, as a practice, interfere with persons who wish to damage themselves as long as they choose to do so through culturally acceptable means.

It would not be difficult to demonstrate, without ambiguity, the extent to which the use of the concepts of danger and injury is highly selective. The point I wish to make is that it is important to consider the functions that psychiatry performs as a social institution and as a representative of various social agencies in the community. It is quite clear what the psychiatrist does when he is the agent of an individual patient who seeks his care voluntarily. However, the extent to which psychiatry constitutes an important system of social control when dispensed through social and legal agencies and private organizations has been largely overlooked. From a functional point of view, there are a variety of psychiatric institutions that perform very different functions and that promote different and sometimes conflicting social goals.

The psychiatrist who must make decisions about mental health and danger finds himself, in many respects, in an impossible situation. Unlike the objective and impartial scientist, the psychiatrist usually is an agent of a particular person or social unit; and it is the psychiatrist's obligation to consider the interests of the person he represents. But in social life, people often have conflicting and incompatible interests, and thus how the psychiatrist will see the situation will inevitably depend on whose interests he identifies himself with. From the perspective of his mental health, it may be best that the patient remain in the community and not be involuntarily detained. But, as we all know, this may not always be in the interests of the spouse's or neighbor's "mental health."

Within traditional psychiatric practice, the difficulty of specifying when "health" and "illness" exist is not very important. The psychiatrist does not seek his own clients: either they seek his help voluntarily because they believe they need it, or they are brought to him by agencies in the community that have identified the person as a case and are no longer willing to tolerate him. From the psychiatrist's perspective, most of these patients required his intervention, if for no other reason than that the patient had become involved in a situation where he defined himself, or others defined him, as a psychiatric case and the demand has been made that he be treated or detained, or both. The psychiatrist, because of his own theoretical predispositions, usually assumes that the patient's problem is a manifestation of some underlying psychological or developmental disorder. He thus directs himself to the complaint concerning the patient's feeling states or his behavior as an indication of the need for psychological intervention and analysis—in the case of the mental hospital, the complaint is usually seen as a basis for justifying detention.

The point that should be made especially clear here is that the definition of the patient as a case is not made by the professional practitioner as an independent expert: it is the consequence of community social processes. This is not the place to review such processes in detail, except to say that persons within the community are defined as cases when their behavior and level of performance pose problems for their family, friends, employers, neighborhood, and community agencies. Thus, involuntary hospitalization follows erratic, unpredictable, and bizarre behavior which is visible, repetitive, and disturbing, and which exceeds the tolerance level of the relevant other people involved (21). Although bizarre persons pose a variety of serious human dilemmas for the social networks of which they are a part, a good many of these patients do not represent a serious danger (in the usual sense of the concept) either to themselves or to others, in spite of the fact that this is often the rationale for involuntary detention (25).

The social institution of psychiatry thus serves the community in a very important way: it supplies a means for discrediting the mental status of persons who behave in a bizarre and "disgusting" way, and it provides a rationale for detaining them involuntarily for the purpose of helping them. The community rids itself of a problem and at the same time justifies its action as a humanitarian act "for the benefit of the patient." Let me say explicitly that I am not implying that psychiatrists on the whole have had anything but decent and humanitarian motives. I am observing, however, that their actions have provided an indispensable service for the community in facilitating the social control of bizarre and difficult persons who posed inevitable problems. Removing such persons "for their own protection and welfare" has provided an easy solution, if not always a just and therapeutic one, for handling these human problems.

I should also mention that psychiatrists have often played similar roles for individuals vis-à-vis the community. Sharing certain values and orientations with particular patients, they have not been unwilling to "bootleg humanistic values" (28). Psychiatrists have been more flexible and less rigid than other specialists in dealing with individual cases, and they have more frequently used scientific language and justifications to promote humanitarian goals and values. While their motives are usually commendable (at least according to my value dispositions), the use of "science" to justify particular value orientations may not always be helpful to psychiatry as a profession (8). More than twenty-five years ago Kingsley Davis, in analyzing the mental hygiene movement—a movement in many ways similar to various current notions of community psychiatry—illustrated the extent to which it was linked to a particular set of social class values and ideals. His paper on the mental hygiene movement (7) applies cogently to various current concepts. He wrote:

We should like to define mental hygiene in terms of its chief aim, but the general goal as usually stated—improvement of mental health in the community, promotion of personal efficiency, or provision for personality expression and happiness—is ambiguous. Mental hygiene hides its adherence behind a scientific facade, but the ethical premises reveal themselves on every hand, partly through a blindness to scientifically relevant facts. It cannot combine the prestige of science with the prestige of the mores, for science and the mores unavoidably conflict at some point, and the point where they most readily conflict is precisely where "mental" (i.e., social) phenomena are concerned. We can say, in other words, that devotion to the mores entails an emotional faith in illusion. . . . Actually the mental hygienist will continue to ignore the dilemma. He will continue to be unconscious of his basic preconceptions at the same time that he keeps on professing objective knowledge. He will regard his lack of preventive success as an accident, a lag, and not as an intrinsic destiny. All because his social function is not that of a scientist but that of a practicing moralist in a scientific, mobile world.

THE INFLUENCE OF HOSPITALIZATION

Mental hospitals in this country have primarily provided custodial care. In addition, these institutions have traditionally been isolated from usual community activities and community responsibility, so that frequently, upon his entry into the hospital, a patient's ties with the community are greatly diminished. Even assuming that mental hospitals provide adequate programs of care—which they do not—there are a variety of dangers in long-term hospitalization that have only recently been recognized. Since such institutions weaken the patient's ties with his community, his future capacity to adapt adequately to the community may be undermined. Further, as Goffman has so vividly pointed out (10), the adaptations appropriate to hospital life that the patient makes may be entirely inappropriate to community life. Moreover, the separation of the hospital and patients from close community contact increases the stigma of mental illness and often undermines community responsibility for providing a mental patient with post-hospital opportunities (31). Finally, the very great emphasis given to involuntary commitment in the United States is probably detrimental to the patient's integrity and often prevents possible therapeutic relationships.

Involuntary commitment is similarly a destructive process from the physician's perspective, since it makes his role relative to the patient ambiguous. To the extent that he is not perceived by the patient as his agent, considerable therapeutic difficulties develop. Traditionally, since mental illness was viewed as an attribute of individual psychological functioning, it was implicitly assumed that the social structure of the hospital and the means of hospitalizing the patient had no particular effect on the course of the illness or on the treatment process. With increasing awareness of the social contingencies of adaptation and disability, mental health workers are increasingly sensitive to the noxious influences of particular institutional arrangements.

The extent to which organizational and institutional arrangements will be viewed as significant components in the treatment of the mentally ill depends, in large part, on the theory accepted by the mental health worker. In evaluating what course community psychiatry should take, it is essential that the theoretical approach be explicit. Thus, before discussing some possible perspectives for community psychiatry, I shall review briefly the social conception of adaptation that underlies my analysis.

A SOCIAL THEORY OF ADAPTATION

Psychiatric theory has traditionally focused on the intrapsychic processes of psychological defense. Mental illness has been seen, thus, as "psychic pathology" or as a dysfunctioning of the "mind." The defenses, as perceived by Freud and his daughter, were denials, falsifications, and distortions of reality; and it was generally assumed that these defenses operated unconsciously so that the person lacked awareness of what he was doing. Although other psychiatrists enlarged this notion of defense and its application, adaptation is still basically conceived of within psychiatry in terms of mental as opposed to social processes, and primarily in terms of the unconscious.

A social view of adaptation takes a somewhat broader perspective: very simply, adaptation is viewed as the manner in which a person comes to terms with his life situation. Analytically, adaptation involves two basic components: coping and defense (23). Defense, as used here, refers to the traditional psychological view of adaptation: it refers to the manner in which a person manages his emotional and affective states and maintains psychological integration as a person. Coping, on the other hand, has been relatively neglected by psychiatry. Coping here refers to the instrumental behavior and the instrumental capacities of the person in meeting life demands. Thus it concerns the application of skills, techniques, and knowledge that the person has acquired as a social being, and it encompasses social learning and the socialization process in general.

There is considerable variety in the extent to which individuals can mobilize instrumental activity for mastery of stress situations. Some situations, like bereavement, largely involve working through the grief experience on a psychological level. In contrast, most life situations of crisis or stress involve the possibility of more or less instrumental behavior, which, if the individual's coping capacities are adequate, allows reversal of the crisis. Psychiatrists, however, have concentrated to a much greater extent on the individual's psychological defenses, and to a much lesser degree on coping capacity. Mental disorders have thus been generally viewed as breakdowns or distortions of psychological defense and integration rather than as deficiencies in coping capacity.

Perhaps the process of adaptation can be described more vividly with a brief example. A number of years ago I participated (with Dr. David Hamburg) in a study of applicants for a coveted psychiatric residency in the Midwest. Candidates for the residency were subjected to an interview that was regarded as a rather stressful experience: they were brought individually before a group of eminent psychoanalysts who were to interview them for assessment purposes. One way of viewing the candidates' performance in this situation was to consider performance to be a consequence of psychological adequacy. Yet, in studying the candidates, it seemed fairly evident that the extent to which they were able to control the "stress" situation was in large part a consequence of the manner in which they had prepared for it and the kinds of information they had obtained about it prior to the interview. Although the data that we analyzed were not amenable to a statistically clear interpretation, they strongly suggested that the candidates who anticipated questions and answers and who were best prepared to deal adequately with the interview were those who had talked with others who had faced similar interviews. Candidates who had not obtained such information, or who had incorrectly anticipated that the interview would be concerned more with their knowledge than with their personal history, seemed unprepared and appeared to experience considerably more distress during and after the interview. Thus the extent to which candidates experienced stress, as well as their performance in the situation, seemed to be clearly related to seeking adequate information, anticipating the situation, and rehearsing answers to probable questions.

Although defense is an indispensable aspect of any model of adaptation, it should be clear that the major function of defense is to facilitate and enhance an individual's coping capacities. The extent to which defense is "true" or distorted, conscious or unconscious, is in some measure irrelevant. The major criterion by which the adequacy of defense is usually measured is the extent to which it facilitates coping efforts: defense exclusively oriented to facilitating mood and self-esteem, which is separate from necessary coping requirements, is usually regarded as pathological. Defenses that hinder the coping process (withdrawal, extreme autistic perception, and the like) are usually regarded as mental disorders because they lead to ineffective behavior. Adequate adaptation, therefore, depends on coping and defense efforts that are consistent with one another and not too far out of line with social reality, as defined by the particular cultural group concerned. Persons who adjust adequately to social demands and suffer little psychological pain are not said to suffer from mental disorders, although there is debate among some analysts as to whether they possess "positive mental health" from the perspective of a particular set of values.

It is obvious that failures in adaptation are not all regarded as mental disorders. But when persons are labeled as mentally ill by others, they are usually so designated because they fail to deal adequately with social demands: they fail to hold a job successfully, to get along with other people, to conform to the standards of behavior expected of them, to conform to usual rules for communication, or to maintain a comfortable state of living.

If we consider, then, the view of adaptation that I have described, it becomes clear that failures in human functioning stem from a variety of physical, psychological, social, and cultural conditions; and specific understanding of human failure requires that we understand not only the person but the particular sociocultural context in which breakdown in adaptation occurs. An individual's ability to cope with his social environment depends on his ability to mobilize effort when this is necessary, on the manner in which efforts are organized and applied, on his psychological and instrumental abilities and skills, and on the extent to which he has social and environmental supports. These in turn may depend on the person's ability to acquire cultural means through learning; the adequacy of group solutions that are culturally transmitted; the kinds of life circumstances with which the person is challenged; and the individual's physical health—to mention only a few factors. Inability to cope may result, of course, from inadequate defense; the person may have the necessary instrumental skills but he may fail to maintain mental functioning adequate for effectively mobilizing his resources in various circumstances. In general, however, an adequate community psychiatry program must deal not only with the patient's psyche but also with the development of his skills and capacities, and with the improvement of his opportunities for meaningful interpersonal relationships and work, through carefully structured and comprehensive therapeutic programs.

SOME POSSIBLE PERSPECTIVES FOR COMMUNITY PSYCHIATRY

Now that an adaptation model has been described, it is important to state explicitly what implications such a model may have for community psychiatry. Some, in becoming proponents of the "crisis" perspective, have encouraged psychiatrists to become involved in social action relevant to all of the human conditions that have undesirable consequences for "mental health" (5). The most enthusiastic proponents of community psychiatry are even inclined to bring mental health to the people, if the people are unwilling to solicit it on their own. Such inclinations encompass a variety of serious problems.

As the abundant literature on "positive mental health" shows (17), it is impossible to distinguish mental health from a variety of other social and ethical perspectives; therefore, it is particularly difficult to specify who needs the "mental health" that is being dispensed, and to what populations and under what conditions it should be provided. Moreover, it is quite possible that in attempting to provide "mental health" through attempting to change community structure, we violate social goals and values that some groups hold more dear than psychological security and social adjustment. There is little doubt that we could eliminate automobile accidents by banning the automobile, or that we could diminish the rate of pregnancy among unmarried college girls by dispensing contraceptives and teaching them how to use them effectively. In fact, we have long recognized that many of the social problems we face are, at least in part, a consequence of our values and of the kinds of goals and the social system we wish to promote. Thus the question we must ask is not whether it is desirable to promote mental health—few would disagree with such a laudable goal. The real question concerns the price we are willing to pay to promote the basic social conditions conducive to mental health, and the price is more than an economic one. It is not at all clear that the cost of alleviating certain "noxious" social conditions would be "reasonable" or "desirable" in terms of our conceptions of individual liberty, creativity and innovation, autonomy, and progress itself. I fear that physicians sometimes forget that health is not always at the apex of our hierarchy of values and goals.

The problems of becoming involved in value dilemmas and conflict are quite foreign to traditional medical and psychiatric practice. In the traditional patient-physician relationship, the patient usually initiates the contact and seeks the physician's assistance voluntarily. Thus the patient defines his own need for help, and although he may subject himself to the physician's influence, it is clear that the physician is his agent and committed to his interests. Physicians do make mistakes in treatment, and they sometimes produce iatrogenic disorders; but these are generally the assumed and accepted risks of the contract between the patient and his physician.

In reaching out to contribute in new ways, psychiatry is faced with some realistic possibilities and alternatives that do not require great transformations of the traditional psychiatric role. Certainly, psychiatry as a profession can encourage increasing availability of resources and personnel for those who wish to seek care, and psychiatrists can work to develop more adequate therapeutic methods that are helpful to a variety of social, economic, and ethnic groups (15). Similarly, the enlarged perspective of community psychiatry that explicitly takes into account socio-cultural forces and organizational influences is useful in individual and group treatment (6). Since a basic goal of therapy usually involves helping the patient to understand his difficulties and to cope with them more adequately, the therapist is inevitably involved in re-education and in providing social support. The implications of a wider perspective for psychiatry are also evident in various suggestions for greater scope in the choice of treatment alternatives; for diversified services that better utilize the social resources of the community (and that are more closely geared to the levels of incapacity that different patients experience); and for a closer relationship, in general, between treatment and community process.

Some psychiatrists are dissatisfied with such developments and with a role as limited as the one I have proposed, and others do not wish to participate in any changes at all. While the latter are threatened by any program that changes traditional practices, relationships, and work activities, the former feel dissatisfied because they consider the kind of program proposed here as "correctional." Those who recommend drastic change in psychiatric roles are impatient, for they insist that they must not only treat the incapacitated but remedy the conditions that produce incapacity. While their sentiments and motives may be commendable, they fail to recognize that the community may not tolerate the psychiatrist as a social planner; and to the extent that the psychiatrist attempts to intervene in public policies and to influence social values, he shall increasingly subject himself and his profession to conflict and political abuse. If psychiatry is to have integrity as an investigative discipline and as a helping profession, its work must be protected from value conflict and propagandistic goals. The use of psychiatry as a science to justify and promote controversial social and ethical goals may in the long run deprecate the adequacy of "psychiatric science" and the usefulness of psychiatry as an instrument of help.

THE FUNCTIONS OF PSYCHIATRIC INSTITUTIONS IN THE COMMUNITY

As psychiatry increases its participation in community life, it will be called upon to perform a variety of new functions. Persons involved in "community psychiatry" should be aware of how various community agencies view them, and they should think through the kinds of roles they wish to perform (14). Psychiatry is the recognized specialty group that assumes responsibility in circumstances involving persons who are defined as bizarre in their behavior or affect. Thus, psychiatrists have served in a diagnostic and helping role relative to a variety of self-defined and community-defined problems. In fulfilling this role, they have worked in the courts, in social agencies, and in government and private organizational programs. Increasingly, however, psychiatrists have intervened not as representatives of individual persons or families but as agents of larger social units. As a result they have become involved in assessing persons for clients who have a variety of interests that may be inconsistent with those of the people with whom the psychiatrist most closely works (29). Even within the best of such organizations, psychiatrists are often called upon to provide justification or a rationale for organizational decisions, or are asked to "cool out" certain undesirables (11). Psychiatry may thus, in some cases, become a means for promoting certain aims, interests, values, and programs that would be much more difficult to promote without psychiatric assistance. Under the guise of science, psychiatry can be used to provide acceptable justifications for various organizational programs; or it can be used effectively to discredit the behavior of persons who come into conflict with the values and goals of an organization. Most public roles involve pressures on professionals of any kind, and the fact that such pressures exist is no reason to retreat from all organizational activity. What the psychiatrist— and psychiatry as a profession—must remember, however, is that the psychiatrist is not the helpless tool of any bureaucracy that employs him; that he has the right, the power, and the responsibility to define his own role and professional ethics relative to the organization within which he participates.

THE SOCIOLOGICAL PERSPECTIVE RELEVANT TO EVALUATIONS OF ILLNESS

In conclusion, I would like to make explicit what a wider sociological perspective can contribute to the clinical practice of psychiatry. Implicit in the clinical perspective is the assumption that patients suffer individual aberrations characterized by defects in physiology or intrapsychic functioning. And it is assumed that such disorders can be understood through an exploration of the individual's physiology or psychology. Thus illness is seen as a deviation of the person from a state of normality.

Perspectives themselves are neither right nor wrong; but varying perspectives raise different questions and open different areas of investigation. From the sociological perspective, the arrival of the patient at a medical context usually comes as a result of a difficulty that the patient has and of a variety of social, cultural, and psychological forces that induce the patient or others to present his case for intervention (20). The clinician, however, cannot easily separate the problems of illness from illness behavior (the manner in which illness is perceived, evaluated, and acted upon), nor can he easily separate the problems of illness from secondary adjustments (disability resulting from social responses and reactions to illness). Within the traditional medical model, the clinician does attempt to make an independent assessment of the patient's difficulty. Through a history, physical examination, and evaluation of laboratory studies the clinician attempts to ascertain whether he can find an objective basis to account for, justify, or explain the complaint presented. Thus, in the classical medical model we have two sets of facts: those surrounding the complaint; and those surrounding the physician's inquiry into the complaint. At least logically speaking, the set of facts that characterizes the patient's pattern of illness behavior is distinct from the set that characterizes the diagnostic procedures.

To take typical psychiatric practice as a contrast, it is much more difficult logically or empirically to distinguish between the patient's pattern of illness behavior, on the one hand, and the facts that determine the diagnosis, on the other. In the absence of a general repertoire of diagnostic devices, the psychiatrist is much more dependent for his evaluation on the patient's complaint or on the social circumstances surrounding the definition of the case. Thus the psychiatrist may diagnose a pattern of illness behavior rather than an objective illness condition.

Having once diagnosed the patient, the typical psychiatric practitioner will usually assume that the patient's complaint arises from some underlying psychological or developmental problem. He thus directs himself to the complaint as an indication of the need for psychological intervention and analysis. But the study of illness behavior implies another possible interpretation of such a complaint: it may be the result of an exaggerated illness behavior pattern or an exaggerated receptivity to psychiatry (27); or its significant aspects may result from environmental factors that exacerbate symptoms. There are certainly some cases where the psychiatrist might more profitably spend his time discouraging illness behavior and teaching the patient to focus less, rather than more, on his psychological state; and other cases where the social contingencies of the disorder are far more important than the symptomatology.

I do not wish to give the impression that a meaningful distinction exists between psychiatric and non-psychiatric practice, although there are some obvious differences. An examination of a typical medical practice in the United States or Britain will show that most of the complaints physicians deal with do not conform to the concept of the application of the medical model as I have described it (16). Much medical practice involves psychosomatic and psychosocial problems and a variety of vague complaints. Another large bulk of practice is made up of acute, self-limiting complaints whose duration will be short regardless of whether there is medical intervention. Thus, what differentiates many patients that physicians see from those who do not appear for treatment is not the presence of disease—since many of the complaints for which care is sought are widely distributed among the general population—but a pattern of illness behavior that differentiates those who seek care from those who do not. The wide differences in the use of the physician in countries with similar standards of health (1) would also suggest that much of medical practice has no great relevance to maintaining the physical health of the nation.

There are some data by which we can assess the extent to which disease is an ordinary condition of everyday living. For example, White, Greenberg, and Williams (30), on the basis of American and British morbidity studies, estimate that 75 per cent of all adult persons report one or more illness per month, and this is a very conservative estimate. Of these, only about a third seek medical care during any given month. Although the severity of disease is likely to be one reason for seeking care, it is well known that a variety of other factors is equally important and that many persons with only very mild symptoms define themselves as ill, suffer disability, and seek attention, while others more seriously ill do not solicit treatment or suffer impairment of their usual activities. Symptomatology and disability are very different aspects of illness, and they must be studied independently.

It should thus be clear that a perspective that views both

patients and nonpatients—their similarities and their differences —provides considerable information not easily available from the perspective of the clinician. In addition to illuminating the selective influences that prompt particular categories of persons to seek attention, this perspective also provides some understanding of the social and cultural influences on risks and outcomes in the treatment process. All clinical decisions implicitly involve weighing the risks and expected outcomes of various treatment alternatives and of no treatment at all (24). Through a wider perspective, such estimates can be made more realistically and more effectively.

A FINAL NOTE ON PSYCHIATRIC SCREENING

Implicit in a number of conceptions of community psychiatry is the value of community screening programs, which are used to detect problems of living in their early phases and as a general device to prevent severe disability (5). Although psychiatric screening may have considerable merit, it should, for various reasons, be cautiously approached. The idea of screening implies that cases requiring help can be adequately identified, and that the risks of identification are small while the opportunity to provide help is great. Such conditions are not always easily met.

Case identification has always posed a serious problem for psychiatrists (2). There is an extensive literature attesting to the difficulty of establishing the reliability and validity of psychiatric screening. Thus we have little evidence that screening can be effectively accomplished. Moreover, we must recognize that there is considerable risk involved in defining a person as ill (26). And there is evidence that in some circumstances the definition of illness encourages and justifies a reduction in coping efforts, especially in cases where motivation for coping is questionable, as military psychiatrists have discovered (9, 12). Thus, in screening, psychiatrists must face not only the problem of defining symptomatology so as to minimize iatrogenic damage, but also the risks of making such definitions. Medical services are used in proportion to their availability; and we know that, for example, in the United States, where people are healthier than ever before in traditional medical terms, they are utilizing far more medical services per capita today and the rate is continually increasing. Similarly, the amount of illness psychiatrists discover is directly related to the criteria used (*19, 27*); and if the criteria are too lenient, the risk of inducing psychiatric "hypochondriasis" is considerable. Finally, screening must be based on the idea that services are to be made available to those who need them once cases are identified. One of the greatest tragedies in the history of psychiatry has been that once patients were defined as mentally ill and sent to mental hospitals, little was done for them. There is little point in screening populations unless services are made available; and, indeed, such screening can have dangerous consequences.

The consideration of screening programs has, I believe, one very immediate and useful purpose. It emphasizes the idea that psychiatrists should mend some of their traditional therapeutic ways. It further implies that psychiatric services should be flexible and diversified, and should be administered on both a long-term and short-term basis. The problems that psychiatrists encounter are many, and there is no logical reason for adopting similar modes of treatment in cases that may vary greatly. Community psychiatry presents a challenge to psychiatrists to orient their services more adequately to the type and severity of the disorders they treat. There is at present in the area of treatment an absence of demonstrated effectiveness. This should argue for exploration, flexibility, and diversity in approach rather than adherence to a dogmatic traditional model.

References

1   ANDERSON, O. Health-services systems in the United States and other countries—critical comparisons. *New England J. Med. 269*:839–43, 896–900, 1963.
2   BLUM, R. H. Case identification in psychiatric epidemiology: Methods and problems. *Milbank Memorial Fund Quarterly 40*:253–38, 1962.
3   BRANCH, C. H. Legal problems related to the care of the mentally ill. *New England J. Med. 269*:137–42, 1963.

4 BRANCH, C. H. Preparedness for progress. *Amer. J. Psychiat.* *120*:1–11, 1963.

5 CAPLAN, G. *Principles of Preventive Psychiatry.* New York, Basic Books, 1964.

6 CLAUSEN, J., AND KOHN, M. The ecological approach in social psychiatry. *Amer. J. Sociol. 60*:140–51, 1954.

7 DAVIS, K. Mental hygiene and the class structure. *Psychiatry 1*:55–65, 1938.

8 Deutsch, A. *The Mentally Ill in America.* New York, Columbia Univ. Press, 1949.

9 GLASS, A. J. "Observations upon the Epidemiology of Mental Illness in Troops during Warfare." In *Symposium on Preventive and Social Psychiatry.* Washington, D.C., Walter Reed Army Institute of Research, 1957, pp. 185–206.

10 GOFFMAN, E. *Asylums.* New York, Doubleday-Anchor, 1961.

11 GOFFMAN, E. On cooling the mark out. *Psychiatry 15*:451–63, 1952.

12 GROUP FOR THE ADVANCEMENT OF PSYCHIATRY. *Preventive Psychiatry in the Armed Forces: With Some Implications for Civilian Use.* Report No. 47, 1960.

13 HALL, J. *General Principles of Criminal Law.* Indianapolis, Bobbs Merrill, 1960, pp. 449–51.

14 HALLECK, S., AND MILLER, M. The psychiatric consultation: Questionable social precedents of some current practices. *Amer. J. Psychiat. 120*:164–69, 1963.

15 HOLLINGSHEAD, A., AND REDLICH, R. C. *Social Class and Mental Illness.* New York, John Wiley and Sons, 1958.

16 HUNTLEY, R. R. Epidemiology of family practice. *J. Amer. Med. Ass. 185*:175–78, 1963.

17 JAHODA, M. *Current Concepts of Positive Mental Health.* New York, Basic Books, 1958.

18 JOINT COMMISSION ON MENTAL ILLNESS AND HEALTH. *Action for Mental Health.* New York, Basic Books, 1961.

19 MANIS, J. G., *et al.* Estimating the prevalence of mental illness. *Amer. sociol. Rev. 29*:84–89, 1964.

20 MECHANIC, D. The concept of illness behavior. *J. chron. Dis. 15*:189–94, 1962.

21 MECHANIC, D. Some factors in identifying and defining mental illness. *Ment. Hyg. 46*:66–74, 1962.

22 MECHANIC, D. Sources of power of lower participants in complex organizations. *Admin. Sci. Quart. 7*:349–64, 1962.

23 MECHANIC, D. *Students Under Stress: A Study in the Social Psychology of Adaptation.* New York, Free Press of Glencoe, 1962.

24 SCHEFF, T. Decision rules, types of error, and their consequences in medical diagnosis. *Behav. Sci. 8*:97–107, 1963.

25   SCHEFF, T. Legitimate, transitional, and illegitimate patients in a Midwestern state. *Amer. J. Psychiat.* 120:267–69, 1963.

26   SCHEFF, T. The role of the mentally ill and the dynamics of mental disorder. *Sociometry* 26:436–53, 1963.

27   SROLE, L., *et al. Mental Health in the Metropolis.* New York, McGraw Hill, 1962.

28   SZASZ, T. S. Bootlegging humanistic values through psychiatry. *Antioch Review* 22:341–49, 1962.

29   SZASZ, T. S. *Law, Liberty, and Psychiatry.* New York, Macmillan, 1963.

30   WHITE, K. L., *et al.* The ecology of medical care. *New England J. Med.* 265:885–92, 1961.

31   WILLIAMS, R. H., ED. *The Prevention of Disability in Mental Disorders.* U.S. Public Health Service Publication No. 924, Mental Health Monograph 1, 1962.

[*Twelve*]

Community Psychiatry
What It Is and What It Is Not

MARTIN B. LOEB, PH.D.

P SYCHIATRY is the scientifically based art of treating mental
disorders and emotional disturbances. It is not a tool of social reform; it is not the panacea for all human ills; and, although
the insights and knowledge achieved in psychiatry may be
helpful in many human pursuits, it is not the apex of humanistic
knowledge. Community psychiatry is the use of community
resources in addition to interpersonal and intrapersonal resources
to help mentally ill and emotionally disturbed people achieve
greater personal and social adequacy. It is the purposive use of
these resources that has in the past been overlooked. Intensive
psychotherapy is not essential to community psychiatry, nor is
supplying psychiatric consultation to other professional people in
community agencies the foremost activity. "Psychiatrizing the
community" by using a psychotherapeutic approach to agencies,
neighborhoods, government, or to social movements that are not
favored is certainly not synonymous with community psychiatry.

NOTE: Material for this paper has come out of work for the Community Mental
Hospital Project of the Psychiatric Institute of the University of Wisconsin, which
is in large part supported by a grant from the National Institute of Mental Health,
No. MH 011–82–02.

But to the extent that these activities reduce the suffering of the mentally ill or specifically prevent mental illness, they are important aspects of community psychiatry (3).

It is in the context of the treatment of mental illness that Leopold Bellak, in his recent work (1), refers to community psychiatry as "the third revolution" in psychiatry. The heroes of the first revolution were Pinel and Tuke, who used humane concern and a total intervention, which was later called "moral treatment," to relieve the sufferings of the mentally ill.

Out of this humane interest came a period of custodial care, but, at the same time, psychodynamic theory was being pursued with enthusiasm. The second revolution was led by Freud and was characterized by understanding and hope. This psychoanalytic era was more scientific than therapeutic: it provided greater understanding of mental illness but little or no significant data to prove the effectiveness of psychoanalysis as a therapeutic intervention.* During this era there was greater interest in process than in goal, in means than in objectives. There were even entertained such absurd notions as "the flight into health," a concept that does not easily fit into any definition of community psychiatry.

If there really is a revolutionary element in the present era, it will be found in treatment processes derived from empirically tested knowledge rather than from wisdom based on practice. This revolution is based more on expectation than on hope, and where community psychiatry is practiced, an accounting for the professional's activity and the community's money will be demanded. Attempts to develop techniques of measuring efficiency and efficacy have resulted in some reformulations of ideas about the objectives of psychiatric intervention. The most important of these has been that the patient should behave more appropriately as a result of psychiatric intervention. This does not take into account what has been referred to as "psychodynamic esthetics." The personality structure which has achieved a proper esthetic

---

* There are a great many references to studies and evaluations of studies to back up this statement. In a paper presented at the Sixth International Congress on Psychotherapy, Dr. Jurgen Ruesch, professor of psychiatry at the University of California, San Francisco, pointed out that psychoanalysis seems to help healthy people but is unproven as a way of helping the sick.

balance is not going to be nearly so relevant as is the behavior or the performance of a patient after psychiatric intervention. The objective is to restore appropriate social and interpersonal functioning. Furthermore, this can be measured. At least, whether or not appropriate social and personal functioning has been achieved can be established. This behavioral criterion reduces the heights to which one may aspire, and that is precisely the difference between hope and expectation. Because of the intervention, something is to happen, and this will determine what is to be done to promote the expectation.

In a sense, we are returning to the approaches of the pre-Freudian period: psychiatry is once again goal-oriented rather than being primarily process-oriented. The difference, however, is that our new approaches are based on scientifically and empirically derived knowledge, and as a result our activities can be both broad and specific.

Psychiatric phases or revolutions grow out of value systems—or actually out of the culture. Cultures are made up of little cults, such as the nineteenth-century cult of the cure, which optimistically sought to discover a way to end all mental illness. The cult of mental health that evolved early in this century is, to some extent, still with us. This cult is responsible for the belief that a patient should come out of treatment better than he ever was before, that he should, indeed, be immunized and remodeled. Another of its notions is that a proper early childhood will provide immunity to mental illness. If a child has a loving mother from whom he is never separated, all will be well. There is still a general hopefulness that we can achieve such positive mental health.

The newest cult seems to be that of rehabilitation. Through this cult we are led to suspect that there is a more or less constant rate of mental illness in the population.* One's mental health may quicken the recovery from mental illness but it will not prevent mental illness. Mental illness is thought of not as curable but as readily amenable to control. There is the possibility of reduction

---

* See, for example: Herbert Goldhammer and Andrew W. Marshall, *Psychosis and Civilization* (Glencoe, Illinois: The Free Press, 1953); and Joseph W. Eaton and Robert J. Weil, *Culture and Mental Disorders* (Glencoe, Illinois: The Free Press, 1955).

in the severity of symptoms and distress and the modification of dysfunctional coping patterns. The modification of dysfunction is the principal aim of rehabilitation, which has limited goals and makes maximum use of tested knowledge.

Stress is a constant reality for everyone, and some organisms are less prepared than others to cope with the world's hazards: some are less prepared to cope with particular stressors than with others; and some are generally poorly equipped and unable to cope well with anything. Intervention by means of drugs or psychotherapy can strengthen the organism so that it is possible to cope with internal stress; intervention can teach the organism how to cope with external stressors, and sometimes it can modify environment so as to minimize the stress (4). These interventions involve removing a causative agent, reducing the hazard, and providing social prosthetics for crippled psyches, even to the extent, in some cases, of providing complete protection.

The activities involved in strengthening and modifying person and community together make up a spectrum of services in the mental health field or, more properly, the mental illness field. Within this spectrum are four basic categories of service: prevention, outpatient care, protective care, and total institutional care. Any community that has some kind of program in each of these categories is equipped to help its mentally ill. The appropriate use of this spectrum of services is the essence of community psychiatry, and the practitioner's skill is the most important ingredient.

Community psychiatry is one of the kinds of intervention or one of the packages of intervention that all psychiatrists and all people interested in the treatment of mental illness have in their little black bags. It is not something done exclusively by "community" psychiatrists. The important aspect of community psychiatry in terms of the use of services is the concept of continuity of care. The spectrum of services might be said to be to psychiatric practice what the pharmacopoeia is to other medical practices. The use of these services in behalf of a patient's health and welfare is the psychiatric prescription, the intervention. Clearly, community psychiatry means not psychiatrizing a community, but communitizing the psychiatrists. The psychiatrist's knowledge of his patients' needs is a great help to community planners and organizers in developing the scope and details of a spectrum of services, but it is not the psychiatrist's responsibility to do all the planning and all the promoting of the development of the services. It is a community responsibility in which many other people and professions must share. Community psychiatry means building the use of these services around the needs of a patient and using the services for each individual patient.

Although the concept of continuity of care seems a simple idea, when looked at as a process it becomes very complex. The spectrum of services translates into levels of sustaining, each with its appropriate interventions and agencies of intervention. Each of these specific agencies has its own efficiencies and deficiencies and guiding a sick person through this intervention system requires the planful use of some or of all its various levels.

The first level of sustaining in mental illness has to do with the person's intimates, the people with whom he is living. These people can be thought of as pathology recognizers or as covert sustainers of the patient. In addition to family members, this group includes relatives, friends, neighbors, and fellow workers— and would also include *self* as one of these intimates. These people are the ones with whom the person routinely interacts and whom he bothers. But even though he may bother them, they will not necessarily recognize what he does as pathological. They may consider him merely a nuisance, but they are often recognized as or accused of being a noxious influence in the etiology of the disease. It is in this primary group that the person with an illness is found, and he may just stay there, to become the problem of the unfound case. Often when a new clinic is opened, such cases suddenly appear. They may, however, be maintained or sustained by their own people in a variety of ways. This primary group also provides the criterion for determining the success of our interventions. Since returning a patient to this group without his being a bother to them is the immediate goal of treatment, an understanding of ethnic, social class, and other differences becomes essential in setting up the objectives of the treatment. Furthermore, these intimates must be involved in the treatment process from the beginning, or else they probably will not be there when

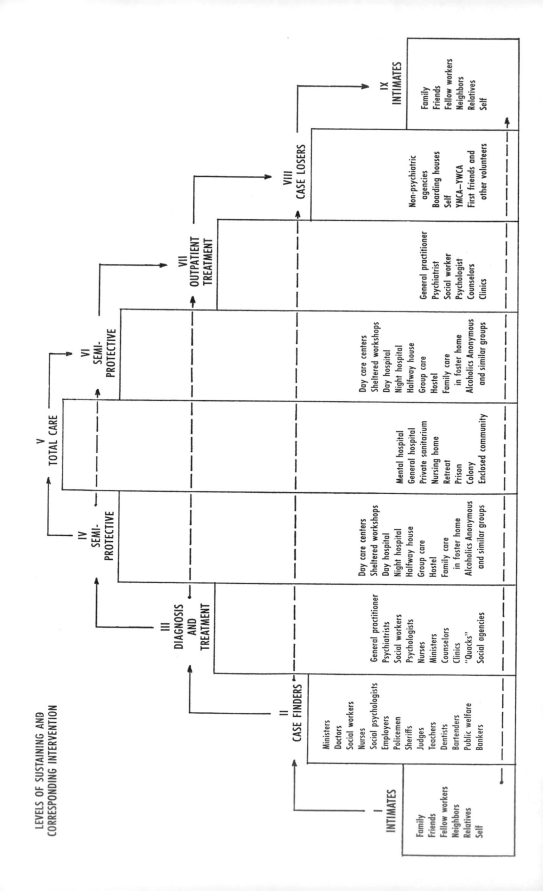

LEVELS OF SUSTAINING AND
CORRESPONDING INTERVENTION

I INTIMATES

Family
Friends
Fellow workers
Neighbors
Relatives
Self

II CASE FINDERS

Ministers
Doctors
Social workers
Nurses
Social psychologists
Employers
Policemen
Sheriffs
Judges
Teachers
Dentists
Bartenders
Public welfare
Bankers

III DIAGNOSIS AND TREATMENT

General practitioner
Psychiatrists
Social workers
Psychologists
Nurses
Ministers
Counselors
Clinics
"Quacks"
Social agencies

IV SEMI-PROTECTIVE

Day care centers
Sheltered workshops
Day hospital
Night hospital
Halfway house
Group care
Hostel
Family care
   in foster home
Alcoholics Anonymous
and similar groups

V TOTAL CARE

Mental hospital
General hospital
Private sanitarium
Nursing home
Retreat
Prison
Colony
Enclosed community

VI SEMI-PROTECTIVE

Day care centers
Sheltered workshops
Day hospital
Night hospital
Halfway house
Group care
Hostel
Family care
   in foster home
Alcoholics Anonymous
and similar groups

VII OUTPATIENT TREATMENT

General practitioner
Psychiatrist
Social worker
Psychologist
Counselors
Clinics

VIII CASE LOSERS

Non-psychiatric
agencies
Boarding houses
Self
YMCA–YWCA
First friends and
other volunteers

IX INTIMATES

Family
Friends
Fellow workers
Neighbors
Relatives
Self

the person, now an ex-patient, is ready to return. Once a patient is taken away for treatment, his people tend to disappear. If they are not there they cannot receive him, and if they do not understand the nature of his disability they cannot help him. Thus, an understanding of this group and how it operates is an important aspect of community psychiatry, and the study of the standards and values of various groups is useful to those in community psychiatric practice. A patient's intimates can provide information for diagnosis, so that his behavior can be evaluated not only in terms of pathological categories but also in terms of the values of his specific culture.

The second level of sustaining is represented by the "case-finders," the socially designated persons who intervene at the point where pathology becomes visible as social breakdown. case-finders, not how to be diagnosticians. Their task is to be able and then to find the appropriate services or at least to announce that help is needed. Among these people are ministers, physicians, social workers, nurses, employers, psychologists, teachers, bosses, policemen, judges, lawyers, and sheriffs. The purpose of consultation with these people is to show them how to be better casefinders, not how to be diagnosticians. Their task is to be able to recognize whether or not behavior is deviant.

At this point in the continuity of care, all sorts of informal decisions are made—decisions not only about deviance but also about where help should be sought. In addition to learning how to recognize deviants—not schizophrenics, just deviants—case-finders should learn where to go to get help and how best to do it: how to take a deviant person somewhere in the squad car; and where or how to help a family get a potential patient to a physician.

Early case-finding is one of the elements of prevention, or at least of secondary prevention. It is an established fact that when a breakdown from mental illness is found early, it can be treated very quickly and social functioning can in most instances be effectively restored. (It is unfortunate that this understanding is used so little. Perhaps the reason is that we are more interested in doing things other than simple restoration.) It has been found in recent wars that something can be done if help is immediately available. Similarly, something effective can be accomplished if the referral services are readily available to the case-finder. In an Amsterdam emergency service, professional staff go out and deal with breakdown where it occurs—while it happens, so to speak —and the restoration rate there is very high.

The third level of sustaining includes outpatient care, professional diagnosis, and treatment. At this point, a rather small group is actually involved in planning treatment on the basis of disciplined diagnosis. This group consists mainly of doctors, who are assisted by nurses, social workers, and psychologists. Some of the latter do both diagnosis and treatment in many health and welfare agencies. Some of them work independently, as do ministers and counselors as well as a large number of quacks. Practitioners of community psychiatry should not ignore the quacks, because it is to them that many patients go.

There are essentially two types of diagnosis. One is the traditional type, which utilizes descriptive categories based on interpersonal behavior and intrapsychic processes. Community psychiatry, however, is more interested in a second type of diagnosis, which consists of discovering potentials for rehabilitation, of deciding what needs to be done for and with the patient, and of utilizing services that are available in the community in restorative efforts. The diagnosis is dependent, then, on the possibilities of combining the patient's resources and the other resources that are available to the psychiatrist. In using strict diagnostic categories such as Dr. John Wing (5) uses with schizophrenia, one not only decides that the patient is, for example, schizophrenic, but one decides what his potential for restoration is, what he needs now, and what he may need in the future in terms of the services available. These estimates become part of the diagnosis as well as of the treatment plan.

Many difficulties appear at this level of intervention, not the least of which are simply financial. Diagnosis and treatment tend to be expensive. Other deterrents to good practice are waiting lists, which are indicative of inadequate services, long distances to clinic or clinician, and the disuading attitudes of the community and of professionals. Another hurdle for many potential patients is that they simply do not know how to behave as

patients. Perhaps there should be courses on how to be a
psychiatric patient. One of the behaviors that is required of
patients, for instance, in outpatient care, is that they be on time
for appointments. In some cultures, being on time is not considered a virtue and may even be considered impolite: some people
must learn how to be on time. Often, as the sick person converts
himself into a patient, he has to learn how to sit for a long time.
Most important, he must learn how to verbalize. In most psychotherapeutic interventions nothing can be accomplished unless
the help-seeker talks and unless he talks about himself. Talking
about oneself is, of course, an American middle-class custom, but
many people find this difficult to do because their cultures do not
condone it. The candidate must also be able to withstand
diagnosis, terminable and interminable. Diagnosis is a favorite
sport in this country's psychotherapeutic haunts. One difficulty in
trying to become a patient during diagnosis is that nobody will
say anything about what is going on. After all the sitting and
waiting, testing and talking, meditating and conferring, no one
will explain to the patient what is happening, and many times
when someone does appear he will say, "The evaluation indicates
a need for treatment." Often it is the kind of treatment that the
clinician prefers, so that it may be but loosely toggled to the
diagnosis so elaborately evolved. Most important, however, is that
if good diagnostic and treatment services are available at the
outpatient level very few patients should have to go on to more
protective intervention levels.

Characteristically, the object of treatment plans in community
psychiatry is to maintain the patient at the lowest levels of
sustaining while working toward returning him to a circle of
intimates. If, however, sustaining at the outpatient level is
insufficient, another level of intervention, which actually builds
more obvious kinds of crutches for crippled psyches, is available.
This level includes services that have not been very well developed in this country, such as hostels and halfway houses—which
here mean halfway in, not halfway out. Also at this level are
services such as day hospitals and night hospitals, sheltered
workshops, individual foster homes and group homes, rehabilitation training centers, day-care centers, and the whole gamut of

highly sustaining and partially protective services for those who need this kind of care. There are, of course, patients who may not get better but may merely become better able to use these kinds of services, possibly for the rest of their lives. Hopefully, however, they will return to a level of outpatient care and eventually, through the case-losers, rejoin their intimate group. These semiresidential approaches, which seem to be effective and efficient, may well be the most important new developments in the care and treatment of mental illness in this country.

The most radical intervention is that which is totally sustaining: this is provided in mental hospitals, general hospital psychiatric wards, nursing homes, retreats, colonies, and prisons, or in what Goffman calls "the total institution" (2). Certainly, there have been many people in mental hospitals who would have been better off in less than total institutions. One of the characteristics of a total institution is that it produces ailments as bad as or worse than those the patient came with. There are various terms for these ailments, such as "institutional neurosis" and "hospitalism." They produce a characteristic stance or view of life that makes the patient less and less amenable to treatment or even to everyday social intercourse, not because of the illness he entered with, but because of what staying in the institution does to him. What is implicit in the idea of continuity of care is the use of all these services differentially, when and only if necessary. Continuity of care involves, for example, using the total institution at times, but not necessarily for long periods of time. People with physical illnesses go in and out of hospitals, on specific medical orders, and are given appropriate care afterward at home, in convalescent centers, and in outpatient clinics. The notion has developed, however, that the patient with a mental illness should be almost if not entirely well when he leaves the hospital, rather than merely able to return to one of the levels of less total intervention. The hospital's specialized function is to provide total care for the shortest possible period, and facilities at other levels of sustaining must be available if the hospital is to be appropriately used.

It is, of course, difficult to know where to start breaking into the cycle of the hospital-community relationship. Pressure for more adequate services must be abetted by stricter functioning of the hospital. Limiting hospital stays to three or four weeks is a tactic that requires the family and the community to plan for immediate aftercare. Commitment for a specific rather than for an indefinite length of time is another approach. Making specialized professional staff available to aid other professionals, such as general practitioners, public health nurses, and staffs in social agencies, allows for the specific delimitation of hospitalization. Opening hospital facilities to the professionals involved in the prehospitalization phase of an illness, as well as to the patient's family and friends, makes easier the implementation of short hospital stays. Relationships and communal bonds are not broken off precipitously, as in the discarding now so frequently done, and isolation can be overcome or avoided. Unlimited visiting privilege is usually an attribute of good community psychiatry and may be viewed as the positive use of the revolving door principle. Unlimited visiting need not, however, be indiscriminately applied, for the psychiatrist and his professional colleagues must retain the ability to be flexible in the use of privileges and facilities for individual patients.

This concept of community psychiatry calls for a re-examination of some aspects of the treatment process. Since community psychiatry is goal-oriented, the treatment process involves establishing definite objectives. In the mechanistic terms of levels of sustaining, plans should be made for the exit of the patient as he enters each level—not vague plans, not evasions such as "it took a lifetime to get sick, it may take a long time to get well," but plans built into the treatment structure. If, for example, hospitals had a team and a process for release of patients as elaborate as most of them have for admission, more patients would get out of hospitals and be prepared for the next steps in their rehabilitation. One of the characteristics of a unit of a social system is that it seeks to perpetuate itself. A release department will thus try to keep active. One of the tasks of a release department is to help people give up the patient role. Since the ability to do this is a major criterion of the success of treatment, it should be an ever-present consideration in the treatment process.

One of the obstacles to a proper concern about release is the time perspective that seems to be indigenous to total institutions. An indefinite span of time can be time without an end. Patients are expected to be there a long time and therefore everyone can take his time. In many hospitals, admission and diagnostic procedures that should quite probably take only a few hours may take a month or more. But why rush if nothing is expected to happen and if time has no end? This time perspective is changed if "getting out" is just as important as "getting in." It is clear that this sense of time is highly modified in hospitals that limit the length of a patient's stay—where, in fact, treatment time does have an end. Hopefully, treatment time can, when necessary, be extended onto a level of lesser sustaining. Shortened hospital stays are possible only if these additional services are readily available in the community: it is almost irresponsible to talk about shortening hospital stays if this spectrum of services is not available.

The present state of knowledge and techniques in psychiatry makes it necessary to consider that some people will remain in total institutions for the rest of their lives. They will remain at the level of most complete sustaining. Some differentiation should be made among or within total institutions, as it is for facilities at other levels. Possibilities other than hospitals are nursing homes and colonies. Some consideration should be given to another type of total institution: the enclosed community, such as the Belgian city of Gheel. In such specially designed communities, the residents could enact "normal" roles as adequately and as often as possible. At present, when leaving the protection of the total institution is a forlorn hope, there is a tendency to let patients do nothing but eat, sleep, and rock or pace or ruminate.

Underlying this approach is the notion that mental illness is a total illness rather than a circumscribed one. Very few people are so sick that they are in fact out of touch with reality. They are in touch with some reality, and in many of their social roles they are at least adequate. Keeping what adequacies there are and enhancing them can help to compensate for whatever inadequacies there may be. The protected community is not the same as a therapeutic community. The therapeutic community, if it means anything, helps patients to get out of hospitals by preparing them for getting out. Sometimes, as it is used in this country, the therapeutic community becomes a way of maintaining patient control—a technique for keeping calmness in the wards. Total institutions of any sort are best when they provide the greatest opportunity for appropriate enactment of social roles, either as preparation for entering the regular community or as a way of maintaining the functions of living.

Although the levels of sustaining that are involved in the coming-out process are the same as those in the going-in phase, there are some distinctions worth noting.

Rehabilitation involves the overt recognition of the presence of a handicap more or less understood. Rehabilitation services, therefore, are predicated on more or less persistent disabilities. Rehabilitation is a substitute for cure. In mental illness, it can lead to such a dissolution of symptoms that ways must be found to help the person give up the patient role. At this level—the going-out level which is equivalent to that of case-finders in the going-in process—case-losers are required. No one knows yet exactly how case-losing should properly be done, although some shoddy techniques do exist—court rehearings, deliberate lack of follow-up of "escapees," and referral to agencies, which do not typically deal with mental patients.*

In Wisconsin a system is developing that can provide help on all levels of intervention and that, by providing a broad spectrum of services, can make possible the practice of community psychiatry. There are a large number of county mental hospitals in Wisconsin. Over 90 per cent of the people in the state are within a fifty-minute drive of a mental hospital. These hospitals were built as custodial asylums; they were not poorhouses made into hospitals but the outcome of special legislation. After two state hospitals had been built, each county was asked to look after its own incurable mentally ill and mentally infirm, and its adult mental retardates. There are now thirty-five of these hospitals, and legislation recently passed has made provisions for changing them into active treatment centers. These county mental hospitals

---

* Volunteers such as First Friends and others who participate in various aspects of patient rehabilitation outside the hospital may be viewed as one type of case-loser.

may be used not only as lifetime communities when necessary, but also as sustaining institutions, day-care centers, day-care hospitals, and night hospitals.

There will shortly be few general hospitals without a psychiatric ward. In addition to psychiatrists in private practice, there are an increasing number of state-aided local mental health clinics. Some communities have halfway houses and hostels, and others are working toward getting them.

In Wisconsin it is possible to move into the practice of community psychiatry in very short order. And it will be possible to demonstrate that the job the community wants done—that of utilizing the best knowledge of medicine and the behavioral sciences to treat the mentally ill—can be done.

In summary, although mental illness may be incurable, it is certainly highly amenable to modification. The best help for the patient will result from having accessible to him all possible resources, and from having professionals who know how to use them and how to help their patients use and relinquish them. This, in essence, is a working definition of "community psychiatry." Community psychiatry is something that all psychiatrists can practice whether they are in public or private agencies or public or private practice. Along with specific therapeutic techniques, it is the practice of good psychiatry.

References

1 BELLAK, LEOPOLD, ED. *Handbook of Community Psychiatry and Community Mental Health*. New York, Grune & Stratton, 1964.
2 GOFFMAN, ERVING. *Asylums*. New York, Doubleday, 1961.
3 HAGLETT, CLARICE H., AND RAPOPORT, LYDIA. "Mental Health Consultation." In *Handbook of Community Psychiatry and Community Mental Health*, edited by Leopold Bellak. New York, Grune & Stratton, 1964.
4 SELYE, HANS. *Stress*. Montreal, Acta, 1950.
5 WING, JOHN K. Institutionalism in mental hospitals. *British Journal of Social and Correctional Psychology* 1:38–51, 1962.

Epilogue

MILTON H. MILLER, M.D.

W HATEVER community psychiatry is, it has taken the profession by storm. This is remarkable since, as professions go, psychiatry has resisted change within its paradigm models of operation despite enormous pressures from many directions over a number of years. Yet within what has been a remarkably short interval, and with an accelerating tempo, a new psychiatric set is staged.

The writers in this volume have described community psychiatry as a variety of interrelated mental health programs, public and private, federal, state, and local, designed to make available to all citizens the benefits of medical, psychiatric-psychological, and social knowledge. The term "community psychiatry" implies a commitment by the psychiatric professional to work in new intimacy with his fellow professionals in medicine, psychology, social work, sociology, the law, the ministry, and mental health administration to provide mental health services to the broadest segment of society. Already, hundreds of millions of dollars have been provided by Congress for mental health programs developed along the lines of the newer community models. We have had described a rich sampling of programs

237

developed in these newer frames of reference, programs that may well serve as prototypes of the many that seem destined to come. Most provide less dependence upon the intensive psychotherapy model than has been the case heretofore. Instead, greater attention is paid to the sociology and epidemiology of disturbed behavior, and the strategic, non-fortuitous deployment of total professional strength has been carefully emphasized. Each of the programs describes the application of techniques designed to offer psychiatric services to the poor and to others in our society who have not ordinarily received them. Efforts are made to provide a full array of interrelated services extending from full hospitalization and outpatient counseling to case-finding and prevention programs in high-risk populations.

Underlying these developments is the assumption that there now exists a body of knowledge and experience that points the way to and justifies development of new programs of social and community psychiatry. But even if this body of knowledge does not exist, arguments have been presented as to the wisdom of moving beyond the data available at the moment and pursuing certain reasoned guesses. This may not be as unscientific as it appears since, as Polanyi has pointed out, intuition, assumptions presuming data for which the data-gathering techniques are not yet available, and a kind of "personal knowledge" have been at the root of almost every major scientific development (2).

Developments during the last twenty months are evidence of the wide support that exists for increasing professional activity in these directions. The first Mental Health Center Act has been passed by Congress, and by the time this book is in the hands of readers, far-reaching supplemental legislation designed to provide funds for staffing these centers will have been introduced and perhaps enacted into law. At the same time, all of our fifty states are engaged in extensive, broadly based planning programs designed to create state plans for integrating existing services and developing new ones. In Wisconsin alone, over fifteen hundred people are actively involved in this planning operation, and it appears that many of the recommendations emerging from the various planning programs will resemble, in one way or another, operations that have been described here.

A somewhat more subtle, though very important, phenomenon is also to be observed within the psychiatric profession. It is evidenced at our meetings, recorded in our journals, and heard in private conversations between psychiatrists. Simply, there is a growing acceptance of the feasibility of a community psychiatry model. Five years ago, most psychiatric professionals did not often think in such terms. Few psychiatric residency training programs offered extensive experience outside of the psychotherapy model, the hospital psychiatry model, or the psychopharmacology model. For many psychiatrists five years ago, the term "community psychiatry" would have sounded as unlikely as a term like "community thoracic surgery" might sound today.

Several doctors have dealt at length with the essential task of modifying existing psychiatric residency training so that young graduates will be able to play meaningful and responsible roles in the emerging programs. Shifts may already be observed within certain departments of psychiatry that have been characterized in the past by exclusive emphasis on the intensive psychotherapy model. Seminars in community psychiatry, chairs in social psychiatry, and an increasing array of clinical assignments in consulting to public and private social agencies are described with increasing frequency in new residency brochures. Post-residency training in community psychiatry is being offered in a number of centers. At the same time, a Harvard-sponsored symposium focusing on the problems and techniques within the community psychiatry model is being conducted for professors of psychiatry under the leadership of Professor Gerald Caplan. This program was oversubscribed when announced to the profession.

Not surprisingly, there may be a corresponding shift away from other training models. Positions in various psychotherapy-centered institutes which were eagerly sought a decade and even five years ago tend to go unfilled today.

William James observed that a new idea gains acceptance in three stages. In the beginning, its critics regard it as absurd and without any basis in fact. As the idea grows and achieves some ascendance, its opponents acknowledge that while it represents a truth, that truth is a minor one, perhaps valid but illuminating only a small area. Ultimately, as the idea becomes widely accepted, its former opponents will say, "Well of course, that's what we've been saying and doing right along." For better or for worse, community psychiatry seems to be approaching the third stage of development.

In an earlier presentation (*1*), Dr. Seymour L. Halleck and I attempted to analyze the factors responsible for our profession's move into this period of remarkable change. Why is this the moment when our profession turns so decisively to the implementation of these newer models of professional activity? Why does it turn in this particular direction, and why now?

We found to be most important the fact that the matter of mental illness and mental health has become the public's business. What has heretofore been something of a closed corporation limited to psychiatric doctors has now become a field increasingly open to inspection at all levels. We suggested that our society no longer thinks of mental hospitals as "their" institutions but, increasingly, as "our" institutions. The growing sophistication of the general public about all medical matters, the impact of television and other forms of mass communication, and the dying out of the idea that some institutions are immune from question (which is increasingly characteristic of our entire way of life) have all contributed to the psychiatric profession being joined by a variety of others in concern for the mentally ill. Many individuals and groups who previously stood aside, deferring to psychiatry, are now actively searching for the role they can play alongside the psychiatrist, or in his stead.

A second factor that has influenced and directed the change within the profession has been the enormous enrichment of our knowledge and the emergence of increasingly effective therapeutic techniques, which are now available to the clinician. These developments have come from chemistry, from sociology, from education, and from a wide range of other physical and social sciences. They bring home unmistakably to the clinician the fact that he is only one, albeit an important one, of the mental health forces affecting the life of his patient.

The fields of clinical psychology, social work, pastoral counseling, psychiatric nursing, and sociology, among others, are experiencing change and expansion not unlike our own. The images of social workers, sociologists, and psychologists have changed, and these groups have become increasingly independent of organized psychiatry. Not only are changes occurring within professions long known to psychiatry, but new professions are emerging. A number of psychiatrists are being trained in the professional skills of sociology, psychology, and the basic sciences. This is not surprising, since discoveries in the basic sciences and in the social and psychological sciences have already challenged and rendered obsolescent any notions of a totally non-biological psychiatry, or of a non-socio-psychological psychiatry. The National Institute of Mental Health sponsors programs in mental health sociology, and many new kinds of training to develop non-medical psychotherapists are reported from various universities.

No discussion of the emergence of community psychiatry can ignore the precise, dedicated, long planned, and enormously effective role of the National Institute of Mental Health. In some ways, the NIMH has acted as a bridge between the total group of health professions, the profession of psychiatry, and society at large. Its importance in terms of what has already emerged in American psychiatry should not be underestimated. The psychiatric profession's willingness to accept many of the principles and programs of community psychiatry into the body of psychiatry reflects considerable priming by the NIMH. Its educational division, its site visitors, its status as forward-looking government at its best, and the respect afforded its leadership (under Dr. Felix and now Dr. Yolles) have all served to influence our profession's readiness for change. While the NIMH, with its current budget of $200 million a year, is many faceted in purpose and influence, its leading role in developing interest in community psychiatry is clear.

Finally, changes within the society and in the world at large, occurring at a pace unknown before in history, have required that mental health professionals look carefully and imaginatively at their professional roles. In this age of mass communication, automation, urbanization, planned and unplanned obsolescence, increasing life spans, and emphasis upon international social welfare, what helping profession could expect to remain static and unchanging?

Community psychiatry may well become an unquestioned fact of our professional existence. It may even have its name shortened to "psychiatry."

References

1 HALLECK, SEYMOUR L., AND MILLER, MILTON H. Psychiatry's place as one of the emerging mental health professions. Paper presented to the American Psychiatric Association, Los Angeles, California, March, 1964.

2 POLANYI, MICHAEL. *Personal Knowledge.* Chicago, Univ. of Chicago Press, 1958.

INDEXES

Index of Names

245

Subject Index

Adaptation, process of, 210–13

Adolescents, day-care services for, 127

Aftercare programs, 4, 58, 107

American Medical Association, 41

American Orthopsychiatric Association, 130

Amsterdam, Netherlands: emergency services in, 230

Anomia, 36

Bronx Municipal Hospital Center. *See* Yeshiva University

Bureaucracy: and the mental health professional, 35–37

Canada: Mental Health Act of 1961, 88; old age pension in, 95; National Institute of Mental Health, 92

Canadian Mental Health Association, 97

Case-finders: techniques of, 59; role of, 220–30

Chemistry: contributions to therapy, 240

Chicago Board of Health, 25–27

Child, neglected: as mutual concern of law and psychiatry, 195–98

Child guidance centers, 17, 103, 116

Child psychiatry, 17

Children: diagnostic services for, 103; state hospital services for, 127; foster care of, 198

Chlorpromazine, 151

Citizen governing boards. *See* Lay boards

Clergy: consultative services to, 80

Cold War, the, 34

Colorado, University of, 102

Community: definition of, 7; casualty-oriented approach to, 65

Community care, 4; effect on hospital population, 93, 94; and family problems, 152

Community mental health centers: barriers to creation of, 31–35, 51–53; and regionalization, 95–98; and mental hospitals, 99–100; development of, in Kansas, 116–18; conceptual framework of, 118–20; services of, 120–24; suggested organizational chart for, 125; jurisdictional problems of, 165–68

Community mental health programs: government participation in, 41, 101, 119; and consultative services, 48, 58–59, 75, 121–22; potential problems of, 60–68; financial support for, 101, 104, 111–12; administrative issues in, 110–11, 115, 129–30; role of citizens in, 117, 119; concept of, 178–81; and legal limitations, 187–88

Community psychiatric practice: preparation for, 177–78

Community psychiatrist: roles and responsibilities of, 9, 170, 171; and clinical psychiatric practice, 9; and social change, 9, 177; and administration, 59, 66–67; orientation of, 61

Community psychiatry: as third psychiatric revolution, 4, 15, 60, 224; development of, 4–6, 133–34, 224–26; 240–41; concepts of, 6–7, 24, 73–75, 165, 170, 176–77, 201, 223, 237–38;